The Speaking Likeness

R. H. MOTTRAM

The Speaking Likeness

HUTCHINSON OF LONDON

01077476

HUTCHINSON & CO (*Publishers*) **LTD**
178–202 Great Portland Street, London W1

London Melbourne Sydney
Auckland Bombay Toronto
Johannesburg New York

★

First published 1967

*This book has been set in Times, printed in Great Britain
on Antique Wove paper by Anchor Press, and
bound by Wm. Brendon, both of Tiptree, Essex*

Contents

1

What makes a likeness speak?

'OHO! You do yourself pretty well in here, don't you!'
Brazier halted in front of the portrait. It seemed
to strike him. I sat down to write the cheque for which he
had called and which I ought to have had ready for him.

'That's my great-uncle.' I thought the explanation sufficient. Brazier is a very decent fellow and his outing for
cripples an admirable idea. But he persisted:

'Is he, though? I didn't know you'd got any ancestors.
What a dewlap.'

'Most gentlemen of that time had a nice frill on their
shirt-fronts!'

'Did they? Pity you don't wear one. Only you'd be so
good-looking I shouldn't like to ask you for a subscription!'

'Well, here it is, anyway. Thank Sir John. He set the
fashion in helping deserving causes!' I edged Brazier along
and held the door open.

'Admirable feller. As good as he looks.'

'Yes. He was. I hope you have a fine day for the
cripples!'

I thought no more of the matter until supper-time, when,
looking at the portrait, opposite, I could have sworn it gave
a slight nod.

I looked at the companion painting of his sister, my

great-grandmother. Less impressive, she was depicted with a slight submissive smile, as well she might be, considering she had thirteen children. One of the younger girls married my grandfather. Thus the two portraits came to hang in my inadequate dining-room. They were painted half-length, but life-size, to hang above some spacious staircase, yet in my restricted space they often seemed living presences. I turned back to that of Sir John, so much the better painting of the two. Was it because more happened in his life, there was more to paint, than in years of patient motherhood?

Yes, there was life in the steady benevolent gaze of the man who, for all the 'deportment' he copied from the First Gentleman in Europe, had so tragic a story, and bore it with such dignity.

I had a feeling that I owed him some amends for Brazier's well-meaning, if uncouth, inquiry that morning, and I gave a decorous nod in return for the greeting I felt he gave me. His shapely, well-coloured face seemed to glow, one would have said, with regular, pulsing life.

'There's something about you,' I found myself involuntarily addressing that presentiment of my long-dead ancestor, 'or Brazier wouldn't have noticed you. He's barely intelligent, though a good sort. I told him to thank you for the cheque I gave him. I told him you set the fashion in helping the deserving.'

This time there was no mistake. The figure of Sir John, in the portrait, seemed to give a slight but unmistakable inclination.

I was not so much astounded as deeply moved. For the first time, in all the years that I have sat before his picture, I seemed to grasp the frustration of those who have been active, and of great sensibility, and are reduced to a mere image of their former selves. With the notion of comforting that dim, deprived shape, I added:

'I spoke up for you!'

From far, very far, away, it sounded, not so much in distance as in the lapse of time, for he had been dead for a hundred and thirty years, I thought I caught the words:

'I heard you!'

Either I said, or perhaps thought:

'I didn't know you could.'

Did those lips, that once spoke to cheering mobs, or to exigent customers in his shop, and on one occasion to royalty, loosen in a smile? So I continued:

'They say walls have ears. I suppose, then, that a living image, which the artist made of you, can have hearing!' There stole into the face at which I was looking an expression that might be confirmation. It led me on, in my queer exchange:

'You know, Great-Uncle, I've so often wished you could hear and speak to me. You and your sister there, living over the stairs up and down which my childhood's steps led me. You always seemed benign. So did she, but somehow she was more withdrawn. Now that I have come to understand at least a little of what life is about, I don't wonder. She must have been preoccupied, with her thirteen children! . . .'

Did he nod? I felt that he did.

'And saddened with losing half of them during her lifetime. I hope the look of me, her great-grandson, is agreeable to her.

'It's a solemn thought, that one's ancestors, such as you and she are to me, may have hoped for descendants that would be a credit to them.'

The old eyes seemed to glow. Did he appreciate that I

had tried to keep my personal feelings in the background, but I did wonder if an ancestor who seemed to have so much more than the average consciousness one attributes to the dead might not be capable of seeing through me and disapproving. So I made a complete confession:

'Of course, the member of the family who means most to me is your niece Sophia, your sister's fifth daughter, my grandmother, and your favourite, or so it seems, for through her I came to possess your portrait, which seems to be speaking to me now.' Hearing my own voice utter such incredible words, I tried to justify myself: 'I am not talking to myself, but to you. You see, Great-Uncle, I know the central tragedy of your life, borne with such exemplary restraint, and never allowed to diminish your usefulness to your fellow citizens, who made you their mayor, twice. And your kindly nature made you an advocate of Reform—reform of all the awful inequalities in the state of our nation, as you knew it—so that, at length, the King bestowed on you a knighthood.'

The old face seemed to me to accept this explanation, with the reticence natural enough to a grief so poignant that it cannot be forgotten in a hundred years, by a sufferer that exists only in effigy and the memories effigy evokes. This stirred me so deeply, more than it had ever done all the years I have sat opposite the portrait, that I closed my eyes in a desperate effort to reach back, through a century and a half, through the impediment of paint and canvas, to the man of my blood, who had been so afflicted and kept his faith in human existence, in spite of every temptation to despair. I heard my own voice wrung from me in sheer urgency.

'I do understand, believe me, why you persuaded your sister and brother-in-law to call my grandmother Sophia, after the woman you loved, who slipped with such passionate reluctance out of life, almost the moment when her little namesake slipped in. I suppose you told the little girl, when she was old enough to understand, why she was called Sophia and what had been the fate of the lovely creature she was, in some slight measure, considered to have replaced. Here I can help you. I know something of my grandmother Sophia. I possess several of her letters to the man she married, my grandfather, just before you died at Brighton. You did know, at least, that she had grown to be a sweet and loving woman. Was that enough? I do hope it was!'

I opened my eyes for a moment, to assure myself I was not dreaming. A rather mournful smile seemed to inform his features. So I went on:

'For, of course, your young niece could not be the Sophia you had lost. That brilliant flame had burnt itself out. It may be that you preferred that partial replacement by a niece named after her. Although I know you were kindness itself to your numerous nephews and nieces, they were not the stuff of which genius is made. None of them, least of all the one you arranged to have christened "Sophia", was capable of embracing a career upon the stage, and dying of the devotion it demanded. As for beauty and the stage, the girls, I feel sure, would have modestly disclaimed the one, and politely declined to entertain the other, finding it enough that their husbands, once in a while, would take them to witness a performance, of Mr. John Brunton's stock company, at the Theatre Royal, Norwich.

'I wonder if my grandmother Sophia's husband ever took her to witness the theatrical triumphs of the eighteen-thirties and -forties? Did she lavish a loving thought on the woman whose name she bore, and who once trod those boards with such promise of distinction, never to be fully realised? I hope she did and spared a sigh for the girl you would have married, making her the aunt of my Sophia, the grandmother I never saw!'

With those thoughts passing through my mind, I woke up. Had I been actually asleep and dreaming all that colloquy? Apparently Sir John had received it with his usual benevolent restraint. Could he hear what I was thinking about that tragic passage of his middle life? I closed my eyes again, for I thought he could. I seemed to hear his voice, muffled by paint on canvas, and dim with a century and a quarter of the grave:

'As I hang here on the wall,' I felt, rather than heard him say, 'I perceive, more or less, the life that has gone on, without me, so changed from anything I knew. Learn from me, Great-Nephew, that our seventy or so years are enough, even too much for us. We cannot keep renewing ourselves as fast as life around us changes!'

'You have no need to apologise, Great-Uncle,' I assured him. 'You were a progressive. You believed in Reform, and were knighted for that.'

'My dear boy,' I seemed to discern his answer, kindly and understanding, as his expression had always appeared, 'it is all so long ago, and from the fact that I have only the perceptions of an effigy, it is a little dim, rather like something perceived in the great leisure of Eternity. But I was proud of my little niece, and her name Sophia was a perpetual reminder of what I had lost, though your grandmother could not be that lovely being after whom she was called!'

He seemed to sigh and fall silent. I understood. If seventy years is too long for the average human to fill with deeds that are in any way memorable, a mere twenty years is so short that such distinction as we can achieve is all the more precious. That is all she had, I knew from the bald, hurried theatrical notices that greeted her acting, and lamented her death. It ran: 'Sophia Goddard was not only a beauty. She had a charm that commanded attention, an intimacy that roused the spectator to share the emotions she portrayed.' I sat back in my chair, closing my eyes, and let my great-uncle unroll for me the feelings, the atmosphere, that he had known eighty years before I was born. Fascinated, I let him carry me back to times I had only read about and tried sometimes to picture. He made them live. He seemed to say:

'I wish I could bring her back, as I saw her, when she played, all too appropriately, the rôle of Ophelia. I learn, as I hang here, that the art of representation on the stage has undergone the very natural changes, without which no art can survive the passage of time. I gather that there is an attempt nowadays to render a character by the aid of details which are called "realistic", and tend to give a passing actuality to what are, after all, figures of drama, of life at some emotional high pressure, and which cannot therefore be real, for no crisis, in its nature, can be prolonged.' I followed his thoughts. 'I must say that my Sophia, as Ophelia, was all too realistic. She was not decked out overmuch with artificial blossoms and weeds, and made to lie in a bath, which I learn as I listen to conversation that takes place among you, is an effort demanded of the unfortunate young women, who, so many years later, have the task of depicting that same character. The fatality which pursued her, and was soon to end her earthly existence, lent all the realism anyone could desire. She knew, even if she fought against her fate, that it would overwhelm her. She did not have to simulate the feelings which were as real as ever Shakespeare could have wished.

B

'You ask, did I desire that your grandmother Sophia should follow more closely her cherished forerunner? The answer is, never. Who could wish any other well-loved young girl so short a spell of human happiness, even when it was enhanced with so much beauty, and ennobled with so much character. For she was happy, and the poignant depth of my tragedy lay in the very fact that when I pleaded with her to forsake the desperate discomfort of her dedicated profession, the unhealthy waiting in damp and draught, for the cue that called her into unnatural conspicuousness from those other moments of sedulous concealments, and to nurse her frail lungs in the comfort and relaxation I could afford and was all too anxious to offer, she would reply:

' "Once the curtain rises, nothing matters! The lights throw their flicker on my gestures. The audience can be seen, dimly, row upon row of upturned faces, whose hunger for emotion one must feed. The play itself lifts one through any petty discomfort!"

'She might have said more, but that was the bitter truth. For the moment, she had a temporary respite in the wings, and then, at last, the moment when I could seek her in those shambling, never properly cleaned or repaired conditions of back-stage, her voice, that could fill the auditorium, and draw such rapturous applause from an audience of all degrees of intelligence, would sink to a hoarse croak, and the figure that mimed with such delicate strength the part she was allotted would be bowed and contorted by the violence of her coughing.'

My ancestor seemed to glow with the reality of his emotions. No varnish, no carefully treated paint could resist the passion that had once shaken his usually well-controlled frame, and came to me in spite of time elapsed and lineaments depicted. I could feel him protest across the lapse of years:

'Can I represent to you, Great-Nephew,' he pleaded, or so it seemed to me, 'the almost physical anguish with which, once we had emerged into the dark street, in rain, or wind, in cold and damp, and she permitted the support of my arm, I felt her too sensitive body shaken by those paroxysms? I would draw her aside into some sheltering doorway, and try to re-wrap more carefully and fully, the carelessly slung coverings her gin-sodden old dresser had fumbled about her. Then she would straighten up, her pitiable little lace handkerchief hidden with what I soon began to fear were the stains of her lethal disease. She would raise her head and take advantage of the shelter of my shoulder, humbly offered. Of course, not every night was windy and wet. I can recall lovely moonlit passages we made between the old solidly-built houses of the City, the frequent parish churches, with great upstanding towers, and lengthy arcades of windows. I have, a hundred times, re-trodden the starlit avenues of the Close, in which she would sometimes choose, as she said, to linger, to rid herself of the air of make-believe of her world of the stage. But her speech, once she had mastered her cough, was not of the handsome house-fronts, or the ancient shapes of Castle and Guildhall, that might have figured in any stage setting.

' "Tell me, John," she would say, "how was I tonight?"

'I was at my wits' end to say something intelligent, and not merely to repeat my devotion to her. I tried, sometimes successfully, to draw comparison with other members of the company. She was generous. "Mrs. Chestnut," she would agree, "has really entered into that part. One feels such ease when one or another, with whom one is playing, lifts the whole representation to the level at which it flows of its own momentum. Do you know what I mean?" I would elaborate sometimes, on such themes, and she was ever willing to listen. And then, and then . . .'

Here the old voice seemed to falter and decline, just as a faulty station on a modern wireless panel faints and fades. I had just the sense to know why. Then his voice seemed to strengthen again:

'I felt as if she were hanging on my arm, a little that she was waiting . . . waiting . . . for however a commonplace, repeated word. I had long said all the admiring things of which I was capable. But I had to find something. Otherwise she would make her own criticism.

' "I felt Mr. Brunton was not at ease. I sometimes fear he misses the more experienced players to whom he has every right to be accustomed!"'

'Her steps would slacken, her acceptance of my arm would loosen, her breath decline to a gasp. Then, indeed, Great-Nephew, I made efforts I can still feel, even as a mere image hanging here:

' "My dear," I assured her with warmth I had no need to simulate, "you don't need to doubt the effect you created, or the support you gave Mr. Brunton. It is all in the pages of the *Mercury*. When you first appeared as Letitia Hardy the London public grew enthusiastic at once, if the critics of the day were less convinced. I have kept cuttings of the records that should convince you."

' "Dear John!" she would murmur softly, "did you keep a copy of what the papers said?"

' "Why, yes, my dear. You know I did. I showed them to you at the time, and I have pasted them in a book for your sake."

' "Did you, John?"

' "I did." She seemed to straighten her figure, and to walk a little faster. I hastened to add :

' "They are all there, for what they are worth. You can see them any day. You know that!"

' "I know you are very devoted, very attached, John. It's a shame to say so, but the fact makes me a little doubtful. You have a feeling about me . . ."

' "A feeling! It is sheer adoration . . ."

' "Lovely to hear you say so . . ."

' "I mean the word in its deepest sense. Can I make it mean more?"

' "No, dear, that is why I hesitate. You see me with the eyes of . . ."

' "With the eyes of love. What more can I say?"

' "Nothing. But if I were another, and not one to whom you are so deeply attached . . ."

' "I mean every word."

' "But if it was another, and not myself for whom you have this foolish . . ."

' "Sophia! . . ."

' "Very well, this delightful fancy, would you not take a sterner view of the way I deliver my lines?"

'Perhaps by this time we may have reached the lodging she occupied, with Mrs. Curtis, in St. Gregory's. Mrs. Curtis was an excellent woman, and opened the door at our knock. She eyed me closely and suspiciously, but when I stepped into the light, and she was able to verify with whom Sophia was standing, she relented :

' "Come in, my dear. Good night to you, Mr. Yallop!"

' "May I not come in for a short time? We were discussing a matter of professional interest!"

' "I don't mind what you say you are discussing. I want the poor girl to have her supper. I'm sure she's famished."

'There would be more of the same tenor. Mrs. Curtis was not only a careful landlady, who whipped off Sophia's outer garments if they were the least damp, and drew up a chair to the fire if the weather demanded it, and stood over her charge, to see her set upon the bowl of steaming broth and the viands that followed.

' "If I let you in, young man, it's not for you to spoil the poor girl's supper."

' "Oh, Mrs. Curtis, as if I should."

' "So you say, but I know what men are. Here she is ravenous, and you'd like to see her starve."

' "On the contrary." I was moderate in protest, for my dear one's eyes, above the edge of the bowl she was dutifully supping, gave me a droll permission to let the good woman ramble on.

' "Then don't let me hear a squeak until she's finished, and this plateful too. Love-making is all very well . . ."

' "Oh, Mrs. Curtis, am I not showing you how discreet I am?"

' "That may be your word for it, but love-making's no substitute for solid victuals!"

'My darling's eyes encouraged me to assent:

' "Miss Goddard was asking my opinion as to her delivery of some of the lines she has to speak."

' "Was she, indeed? Does she think she'd find any comfort in what your feelings made you say?"

' "That's just what she was telling me!"

' "And very good sense, too. Now my dear, here's a nice chop and potatoes . . ."

'The lovely head with its ringlets was shaken at me. But I refrained from addressing her, for Mrs. Curtis was plainly right. The air of strain, of courageous recovery from an effort all too much for her frail stamina, was giving way to a more normal glance and a rewarding satisfaction, as the good food began to give its ease to the overwrought muscles and limbs. Meanwhile the attentive old body had got rid of the outdoor clothes, while never taking her eyes off the plates and dishes set on trivets round the hearth.

' "I don't want to hurry you, my dear. You take your time. You've been wanting what you now had, long enough."

' "It's all delicious . . ." Sophia would say, only to be interrupted:

' "Well, you seem to have made a clean sweep of that lot. Now here's this nice pudden!'

'Sophia threw me a smile concealed with all the art of which she was mistress, as she heard the familiar local vulgarisation of the word.

' "Don't you tell me nothing about it. You eat it all up, every crumb, and the sauce. That'll tell me if it's good quicker than anything you can say."

'I withheld myself with an iron grip, while there was any of the nourishing stuff unconsumed.

'When at length Sophia sat back with a hearty sigh of contentment Mrs. Curtis busied herself clearing away and gave me just this much gracious consideration:

' "Now, young man, you know that you're only allowed here because the young lady's aunt thinks it's good for her to have a little civilised conversation after all she's been through. You've got just the time it takes me to wash and wipe the dishes, and then you know you'll be shown the door!"

'Thus permitted, Great-Nephew, you can imagine I needed no other bidding. Not only was I given this formal leave from old Mrs. Curtis, but my dearest stretched her pretty feet to the fender, eased the cushions of the big chair to which Mrs. Curtis had drawn up the supper table, ran her long delicate fingers through those clusters of curls that framed her lovely face and heaved another thankful sigh.

'But this time it was not the sheer physical relief from exhaustion, want of food, and the exercises of all those intimate faculties through which violent emotion, and not only violent but simulated emotion, supplied by authors, of lines she had to speak, found expression in the rôle she had portrayed. Now, fully fed and relaxed, she regarded the blazing fire Mrs. Curtis had built up whenever the weather demanded it; or, in the milder months, the sparse traffic of those days, in the street below, where moonlight, or the fitful gleams of lamps that some householders had set up to ease their own exits and entrances, for in those days there was no public lighting visible. Those who could, had it, for their own safety. Those who couldn't, went without. With superhuman effort I held back the endearments I would so eagerly have lavished. For I knew they were not invited. Even if they were presently permitted, her mind, at ease even, was busy with measuring the success, or otherwise, with which she regarded her work that evening.

' "Tell me, John. I want something a little more . . . what can I call it . . . encouraging! The lines of Mrs. Centlivre . . . are well enough liked, I know. But would you think me presumptuous if I said, to you only in private, that somehow I have to carry all the burden of interest, like a bodily weight, on my shoulders?"

'What was I to reply, Great-Nephew? You have not read Mrs. Centlivre's *Belle's Stratagem.*'

'No, Great-Uncle, I can't say I have more than glanced at the pages.'

'I can well believe it. From what I have heard of the conversations on the subject in this room of yours, I gather that the authoress of those sometime famous pieces is not often sought on the dusty shelves on which her once celebrated works repose.'

'I suppose they were celebrated in the day when you saw them portrayed by Sophia Goddard.'

'Undoubtedly. But perhaps those also, who, like that beloved girl, are doomed to an early relinquishing of life, have perceptions mercifully sharpened by the All-seeing Providence Dr. Enfield preached about so eloquently. Anyhow, all I can tell you at this lapse of time is that, even in that day, my Sophia seemed aware of the changefulness of public taste and the brevity of the more resounding reputations. I had to use the greatest restraint, Great-Nephew, for in spite of the praise lavished upon her, and, more important, the readiness of managers, not only in Norwich, but at Drury Lane, to employ her, the darling was instinct with modesty, and only too ready to be discouraged. I had to hold my peace, and help her, if and when she felt equal to the task, to say what was in her mind. At length it came haltingly out:

' "John, would people laugh if I were to appear in the part of Portia, in the *Merchant*?"

'My instincts were to blurt out my feelings: "If I come upon anyone laughing at you, I will . . ." Words failed me, for they were inopportune. I schooled myself to answer:

' "My dearest, how lovely! How the dignity and force of Portia's great speeches . . ."

' "Yes, John, dear, so you say, but . . ."

' "I will say something quite different. I may be blinded by my feelings. But if Mrs. Brunton is not well enough you know her husband will not scruple to say so, if he thinks you are not equal to the task!"

' "That is true. Naturally enough, he would select Mrs.

Brunton before me. But it is no secret that she is indisposed, and will be obliged to confine herself to light and minor parts in the ensuing months. Do I make myself clear?"

' "Yes. So, for reasons that will cause no jealousy or ill-feeling, you hope that you may be given an opportunity for which you are too modest . . ."

' "Oh, John, I am the most attached, most admiring of Mrs. Brunton's friends. But it is possible that, rather than go to the expense of bringing down a lady from London, he might think well enough of me, and his wife might not be unwilling to see me as her substitute for a brief period."

' "And you would like the part of Portia?"

' "John, it is a part in which one can feel oneself expanding to one's utmost, to fill out a superb figure that is as light to carry as lesser parts are heavy and discouraging. Think of the great speeches of the trial scene! They almost say themselves, and the public respond to what they feel to be an appeal to their better natures!"

' "Then seize the chance!"

' "That's what I want to hear you say, John. Your attachment that I value so much gives me just the extra fillip I require. If I am favoured by the chance, you will see a very different creature from the one who has, quite rightly, so often been offered the leavings that better players disdained."

'There fell a moment's silence between us. But I was so jealous of any loss of the brief time I was allowed before Mrs. Curtis would return, declaring that she had finished her wash and wipe, and that her dear girl would be better in bed, and so dismiss me, that I was unable to hold back the urgent appeal I felt I must make.

' "Dearest," I sank on one knee beside the chair in which she was taking her so needed repose, "if it should be possible that you are allotted the part of Portia in Mr. Brunton's forthcoming presentation of *The Merchant of Venice*, will you then feel that you have sufficiently established yourself, at least for the present . . .?"

' "I can't say that I should ever feel that, John!"

' "My dear, you have already had enough experience of the life of the boards to know that success is precarious, and sometimes short-lived, and that time never stands still. Surely, once you have played Portia . . ."

' "Ah, my dear, that is not even certain, and, if it were, it would nerve me to attempt one or other of the really great parts that any actress hopes to attain before, as you say, time and chance . . ."

' "But will you always be looking higher, and further . . .?"

' "Oh, no, dear, I trust I have always been modest in what I thought I might accept as within my powers. For instance, I have never made any attempt to put myself forward for Lady Macbeth or for the Merry Wives, or Olivia or even Beatrice. There are so many parts never within my age and capacity yet. Wouldn't you like to see me as Richard's Queen? Or Hermia or Helena? I have even hoped for Miranda, and sighed to be asked to undertake Celia or Juliet or Rosalind. And been accorded, as you know, the place I must still accept as the one I am justified in trying to fill. Audrey perhaps, Nerissa . . ." She had risen, her colour flooded back into her cheeks. I stood up and offered my arm for her support. But the fatal excitement I so dreaded had taken possession of her. The most I was allowed was to feel the throbbing of her heart beneath my hand, as I sought to calm her and lead her thoughts away into the very opposite direction, in which I hoped to guide them.

'I gently helped her back to her comfortable seat, and, taking the chair beside, I did my utmost to put the case for a very different future.

' "You know, my dearest, that I am prejudiced."

' "I fear so, John." She laughed and it was a relief to see her seated again, to hear her tone return more to the normal.

' "... I would stand all night, as I know members of the audience are willing to do for Mrs. Siddons ..."

' "Aren't you tempting me with visions I almost fear to hope to see realised, John?"

' "Very likely, for that is what I want to suggest. Wouldn't you be much more probably the choice of Mr. Brunton, or some other manager, dare I say, if you withheld yourself for a short period? Can't you see Mr. Brunton ... or perhaps it might be Mrs. Brunton, with whom I am so glad to learn you are on good terms ... asking, 'What can have become of Sophia Goddard?' They might even say: 'Let us hope she hasn't had an offer from Drury Lane!' "

'This was evidently the right line of approach, for it caused her to rock with laughter:

' "Oh, John, John, will you never get over your absurd delusions. There are, I dare say, scores of girls ready enough to take any part they are offered, down here where competition is comparatively light, or in London, where there is plenty. Often I fear for the very worst motives." Her face grew serious. I knew all too well the sort of competition to which she was referring, the all-too-easy-going young women, who thought of a life on the stage as one of idleness and rapid success due to the all conquering nature of their non-existent charms. Had I not seen all too much of the empty-headed young females, eager to offer what they felt compelling opportunities to unscrupulous managers?

'My thoughts were distracted by the fact that the hearty enough amusement I caused, brought on one of those fits of coughing which were, to me, a nightmare. For a few moments her delicate body was racked by spasms that were all too searching and forced me to disclose projects I was trying to wrap in allusion and suggestion :

' "You see, my dear," as I tried to soothe her, and gradually helped, or so I liked to feel, the command she maintained so precariously over her all too frail frame, "you need a thorough rest and a period of recuperation. You would be so much nearer your aims if you would accept advice!"

' "Ah, John, I know only too well what your advice is going to be. Resting to me is all too like rusting. When I am not studying a part, or at least hoping to be told to study one, I am only half alive."

' "That's just the point, my dear. I know too well by watching you in the glare of the footlights, and fetching you from those draughty corners in which you have to hide waiting for your cue, that you are, as you say you feel, more alive. In fact that is excitement . . ."

' "Call it by what name you will, John, do you know what mine would be?"

'I curbed my impatience by a violent effort. She struggled out of my arms that tried to detain her, and I rose beside her. She put her lips to my ear and her scented ringlets brushed my face as she whispered the word :

' "Glory!"

' "Too much so!" I could not refrain from saying.

' "Never, John dear, if you love me . . ."

' "Darling, what am I to answer?" I put my arm round

her and strove to draw her gently back to what I hoped
was an attitude of at least some partial repose. I could feel
her heart beating in slightly irregular excitement as she exclaimed :

' "Yes, I know. I do value your attachment, believe me,
John. There are moments when there seems to be little else
in the world, and I do accept what you say and I believe
you feel. I let you take otherwise unpardonable liberties . . ."

'In fact she obeyed by sinking back into the chair, under
the urgency I tried to put into my embrace. She let her
head sink on my shoulder, and I heard her lips, before
mine, forming the words, with all too much of that hollow
resonance, that was often so effective on the stage, but which
in the physical intimacy to which I was permitted had an
all-too-ominous ring. Her words were kind enough, but
their import I felt to be nothing less than fatal.

' "You must not try to distract me from my destiny. I
don't seem to be able to convey to you what I feel about it,
and I certainly cannot confide in anyone else for fear of
being laughed to scorn for sheer presumption. I must throw
my whole life into my acting, John!"

'This seemed so crucial a saying that I felt bound to
answer her as gravely as she spoke, trying all the while to
persuade rather than to appear to command :

' "Do you not sometimes feel that by throwing your whole
life, as you say, you are shortening it?"

' "That, of course, I don't know . . ."

' "Have you nothing to guide you?"

' "The excellent advice of the physician you did persuade
me to see last year was all too like your own, John. I could
not explain to him that, once the curtain is up and the lights
are lit, and I move forward with the other players to deliver
my lines, I am not living less, as he seemed to think. I live

more. I have often told you, once I step into that other world, nothing matters!"

' "Nothing! But what you feel to be an extra allowance of life poured into you by those artificial circumstances, is, in fact, a deep draught drawn from your resources. It may be exalting you at the moment ..."

' "The very word, John!"

' "But you have less left for next time, and I fear, only too vividly, that one day or another you will find you are at the end of what you give with such prodigal generosity."

' "Then, John, I would say, so let it be. So long as I feel I have given of my utmost ..."

'This brought me near to my own limit of endurance. I let my head sink upon her so cherished one, I could hardly restrain my tears and while I was able to control my lips, and not to descend into mere argumentativeness, I think that her exquisite sensibility, that was the making of that very distinction that managers and fellow actors recognised in her, made her aware of my feelings. For she raised herself, disengaged herself from me, and pressing me back upon the chair beside her and seizing my wrists in her hands, she confronted me, not only with deep affection, but with that conviction that the consummate practice of her art lent to her most casual gesture:

' "John, dear!" she said in her most melting voice, "I treat you abominably ..."

'... Nor could I stop the flow of her words ...

' "I know I do, you are so patient and so good. I am what censorious people often describe, quite wrongly, as an abandoned female. I am so, to my own profession. I am only half a human being, dear John. You have made a wretched mistake. You should never have fallen in love ... at least that is what you say, and I believe it ...

with ... a creature whose real life is on the boards, and whose existence is lighted not by sun and stars, but by tallow dips ranged along the ledge of the orchestra and whose actions are dictated by lines of verse, when we are lucky, and balderdash when we are not. Our very hair and complexion is discardable ..." but here I broke in:

'Stroking that lovely head of curls, and smoothing those cheeks she had so sedulously cleaned of her make-up, I heard her say:

' "Give up, John. Give up, while there is time. Serve some woman who can repay you in the very coin in which your open heart is so lavish ..."

' "Sophia, you know as well as I, that these things are not a matter of cool judgment and deliberate choice. I am as deeply constrained to love you as you are, you say, to devote yourself to the life you admit has elements of artificiality, and can sink to the lowest level of public appreciation as readily as it can rise to the highest ..."

' "I cannot choose, John. I might refuse Mr. Brunton, even call Mrs. Brunton to aid me, and decline some part he offered. I might even attribute refusal to your pleadings. You know he approves of you, and has never put an obstacle in your rather frequent seeking of me in my dressing-room. But how many times dare I fail to justify the choice he has made of me, even when it is little more than a walking-on part? Think of his week's programme to be filled, parts allotted, rehearsals fixed. How soon would he begin to say, kindly enough, no doubt, and perhaps in consultation with his wife, 'Well, Sophia Goddard was indisposed last week. The week before she declined to act, when we were in some straits to put on *Lovers' Vows* and *Raising the Wind*. I begin to feel I cannot rely on her, and must find someone upon whom I can call with confidence!'?"

'I listened, disheartened, to this reasoning. At that moment, before I could think of some means of renewing my appeal to her, Mrs. Curtis came bustling back.

' "Now, young sir, you know the young lady's friends and relatives think she ought to have every care and attention. If you've said all you've got to say . . ." Here the good woman, whose heart was as soft as her Norfolk speech was sharp and summary, gave us both the serio-comic mixture of frown that descended upon the forehead, and broad quizzical smile that enlightened the firm red lips, till we both burst out laughing:

' "Never, Mrs. Curtis. It's most kind of you and I do feel grateful, but I shall never find it easy to say all I have to say to this particular young lady . . ."

' "I dare say," came the retort. "There's many a knot tied with the tongue that can't be undone with the teeth."

' "I must say, Mr. Yallop is always full of the most agreeable subjects," Sophia put in, her dear eyes dancing with fun, and the easy good humour in which she was adept enough rising with no need for simulated mirth.

' "I dare say, I dare say," Mrs. Curtis rejoined, folding her hands, red and roughened with her domestic task, on the apron she had not discarded. "All about politics, no doubt. They say the Whigs will gain the upper hand, but what I say is, how much will it cost them!"

' "Oh, Mr. Yallop is against all corrupt practices, aren't you, John?"

' "Yes, indeed. I am convinced . . ."

' "That's what you've been telling the young woman, no doubt, these twenty-five minutes by the kitchen clock."

' "Oh, can it be as long as that?"

' "Well, you know, my kitchen clock is never wrong. How would I get my young lady's supper ready in time if it

c

were? It's no good looking at that one in the corner. It's never been the same since my poor husband died!"

'Sophia and I knew this allusion so well that we both joined in our commiseration, hoping to prolong our interview.

' "We do understand your feelings, Mrs. Curtis." The dear girl put on her bewitching smile, inclining her head ever so little to one side, in the practised trick that lent so many stage cajolements their attraction.

' "I'm sure Mr. Curtis did not approve of the way the opposite party try to influence the electorate."

' "My husband used to say that half the Free men didn't know what they were voting for, and the other half knew only too well!"

' "And what was that?" Sophia slipped in the query with that air of the natural inevitable that made of so many set speeches a life-like dialogue when she had tedious parts to perform.

' "He used to say that he knew a good woman who lived in Ten Bell Lane, you know, next the gates. And when any of the gentlemen in politics went to see her husband she put him under the table and pulled the cloth well down. Then she used to say:

' " 'He's not in just now. Can I give him a message?' Then would come a lot of palaver—just as no doubt young Mr. Yallop has been giving you, my dear." Here Mrs. Curtis permitted herself a good broad wink that reduced both of us to attentive laughter.

' "And the good woman used to say, 'That's all very well, mister, but what's it worth?' Then there'd be a lot of fine talk about how they couldn't possibly offer Means, as they called them, for her husband's vote, because if they did the other side might get to hear of it, and set up a petition to unseat our member. So the good woman used to say, 'Well, I've got to wind up the clock; while my back is turned, I shall not know what you put in that old brown teapot on the mantelshelf. But my husband always looks there, to see if I've put back the key of the clock!' "

'By this time we were both dissolved in laughter, but Mrs. Curtis had put on what she called her "straight" face, and, in reality, to get finished for the night with her task of keeping her rooms as they ought to be kept, and I obediently went for my hat.

' "Wait a moment while I unbar the door!" said the kind-hearted old soul. She meant that she would give us the time it took to loose the heavy chain that ran in a slot, and only permitted the door to be opened a few inches. Under this well-meant, if somewhat obvious, pretext Sophia would allow her head to rest a moment on my shoulder, and my arms to be entwined around her, while she joined her loving hands behind my neck. At the sound of the chain falling, we released each other, and Mrs. Curtis would say, as I descended the steps:

' "Good night, Mr. Yallop. Sleep well, pleasant dreams. I'm now going to put a hot brick in the young lady's bed, same as I did when Mrs. Siddons used to stay here. So you'll know she's well looked after." With this dismissal, and a last wave of the hand from my dearest, behind the broad back and smiling face of Mrs. Curtis, I used to turn reluctantly away. Starlight, moonlight, pouring rain, or howling wind made little impression on the image I carried in my heart, as I trudged home to the old house in the Gentleman's Walk, where I lodged above the shop, ever since my parents moved out to Bracondale.'

'It is true that there were occasions when my most cherished thoughts were interrupted. It had even occurred at times that I would be accosted by the wretched street-walkers of those days. For Norwich was not merely a Cathedral City. I hope that noble building still dominates your skyline . . .'

'I assure you it does, Great-Uncle. I would even dare to suggest it is in better repair than it was in the days when you used to look up at it, for the present Dean and Clergy have spent a hundred thousand pounds on its repair and renovation!'

'Never too much, Nephew. I used to gaze up at that soaring spire that seemed to travel across the wind-blown clouds like the mast of some voyaging ship in full sail!'

'I have often thought the same, Uncle, but have you gathered from all that has been said beneath your portrait, these hundred years, that ships no longer pass in full sail? They go by steam, and nowadays by oil, with a steadier, if more monotonous motion, the tower and spire of the Cathedral cannot recall!'

'Can that be? But my thoughts were of another nature altogether. The House of God, of my day, not only looked on citizens like myself and good Mrs. Curtis. It looked down, for almost as long, on a garrison town. And young officers were among my best customers.'

'I expect, Great-Uncle, they hadn't much to do, after the morning parades, and on occasion, now and then, they were called upon . . .'

'My dear boy, don't you realise that young officers of my day were continuously on active service? I have heard that you have had your wartimes. I know you discussed putting my portrait in some place of safety, for fear your house might be demolished by some form of long-distance gunnery . . .'

'Bombs, dropped from Flying Machines, Great-Uncle!'

'Can that be so! Well, in my day there was threat of invasion by great fleets carrying armies across the Channel or the North Sea. The young officers were more likely to come to my shop to buy keepsakes for the ladies they loved and had to forsake . . .'

'I can well believe it. I know, Uncle, what it feels like to say goodbye, and never know if one would survive to greet again a loved one, who might have been the partner of one's life!'

'So I gather. There were some who were not so particular. I have known times when, leaving Mrs. Curtis's establishment, I have been accosted by young men in uniform who had been trying to drown their troubles, or evade the uncertainties of their future. They might have learned by some means that Mrs. Curtis lodged performers at the Theatre Royal, and might assume that the uncertain employment, the shifts and chances of theatrical life, would render the ladies of the company complaisant to offers of some brief and passing affair. If I were asked for the whereabouts of Mrs. Curtis's lodging by young men whose intentions might or might not be strictly honourable it seemed to me more appropriate, although I knew Mrs. Curtis's front door was defended by that heavy chain, and her back door by a rough mongrel dog she kept chained up during the day and left to roam her yard at night, to give such inquirers another address, in the little square behind St. Benedict's Church.'

'That, I'm afraid, Uncle, was destroyed by the vicissitudes of aerial bombardment in 1942 . . .'

'Perhaps, my dear boy, it is just as well. For the tenant of the premises, in my day, was a person known in Norwich as Old Molly. I do not know if she had, or ever had had, any other name. It was sufficient for the purposes for which she used it. Any inquirers whose attentions to Mrs. Curtis's guests I might deem unfitting and unwelcome were far more likely to find what they were looking for at such a place. At any rate, I was spared all anxiety on the subject.'

Here I forget what exigency of normal life ended, for the moment, the strange interchange I had with my long-dead but so really and actually present uncle. He faded back into his portrait and I went forward to whatever demanded my attention.

2

Dr. Enfield's advice

WHEN I next had leisure to sit down in front of the portrait of my uncle, to see if I could decipher something of his tragic love story that he bore so manfully, I seemed to find him in a different mood.

What governs our moods? Weather obviously, circumstances probably. Perhaps heredity, though I have heard this warmly disputed. Does a quiet conscience or the reverse, a sudden loss of a friend or relative in the ranks of the living, or some event of domestic or world politics have any effect?

Any or all of these factors may have influenced my uncle. All I can say is that on this particular autumn evening, when the lovely light played tricks with the paint on the canvas, it seemed to me to show him in an utterly different frame of mind from the previous impressions I had gained from so similar a contemplation. This time I could almost hear a sigh. I seemed to discern a glance, affectionate as ever, accessible, I dared to hope . . . as before.

And yet, and yet, so mournful!

It made me increasingly careful how I tried to evoke some communication, if I dare call it such! There, plain enough, was the oil-painting by William Hilton, so familiar that it had taken years to penetrate my obtuse senses, and give me a feeling as of interchange of speech, with my long-dead uncle. And now I wanted more than ever to know something of what he had felt all those years ago. I had made a beginning, and I did not know how to continue.

After some moments of silent interchange of our glances I ventured:

'Uncle, I thought I heard you sigh!'

This time there was no mistake. There was a long intake of breath, and its subdued, slow expulsion. And again, it seemed to me ... mournful! I couldn't bear it. I didn't even know if something I had said or done might have wholly or partly caused it. I tried to make amends.

'Believe me, I don't try to know something of what you may have felt, from vulgar inquisitiveness or just idle curiosity. Your feelings mean as much to me as those of any of my own family. Doesn't it give you any sense of support that after more than a century someone should care?'

This seemed the best line to take. For, unless it were some trick of the light, the handsome benign features seemed to soften, and once again I felt I was able to understand something of which he seemed to wish to make me aware.

'Thank you, Nephew!' at first very soft, faint as with distance and muffled as, after all, it must naturally be by paint and canvas. 'It's just age, that is all. You are growing older yourself. You've already had more years on earth than ever I had. You must know what the process of ageing really amounts to!'

'Yes, indeed I do. I've been lucky. I wish I had a penny for every bullet that missed me by not more than six feet. I should be richer than ever you were, with your grand stroke of luck in the Government Lottery.'

Here this intimate allusion seemed to strike home. I thought I discerned a sudden momentary lightening of the sombre mood that had seemed to invest the portrait. He appeared to grasp my words.

'But you know, all the better, that your good fortune in escaping the risks of the battlefield makes little difference forty years after. You will join us, the great majority. You will even be fortunate, if you have, as I have, a portrayal of your mortal features and figure to tell posterity how you appeared to sight.'

'You are right enough, Uncle. We don't have our portraits painted life-size and half-length, as you did. We don't deserve it. Royalty doesn't bestow on us the honour of knighthood, and it has lost some of its prestige since your day. But there has been no real cause, such as that of the Reform that you espoused, to call most of us to the notice of our rulers. Some of my generation and of the next have been liked in life, regretted at their death and have stones erected over them. One at least of your descendants was awarded a Distinguished Flying Cross. That is how honour came to the war-scarred generations that have had to support the vicissitudes of the first half of the twentieth century!'

'Those generations will rise and pass away, Nephew. Will those that succeed be less bloodthirsty, or, even if they are innocent, will they leave a more permanent mark on the long, devious history of mankind?'

'Well, I am a convinced optimist, Uncle. I think you should be too. For as you hang there you have heard enough of what goes on in this room to be aware that the frequent mortality, the miseries of the poor, the gamblers' chances of the wealthy, have all much lessened since your day. And partly, I like to think, by the efforts for which you were knighted!'

'You flatter me, Great-Nephew. I must admit a small

satisfaction in the fact that I did not shirk uttering a then unpopular opinion!'

'Perhaps that is what drew the attention of your gracious sovereign to your merits, Great-Uncle. For I have learned this much in my, as you say, already long and, I admit, fortunate years. There is no means of attracting public, and even well-informed notice, so sure as to utter opinions that are unpopular at the moment, but which are going to be popular with the next change of common sentiment. You saw so clearly that all the preaching and praying that went on, in your day, to congregations much larger, of worshippers of a continuous weekly habit than is the case in the nineteen-sixties, only touched the fringe of the great morass of destitution and need in which more than half the population of the towns and all the villages of the countryside were submerged!'

'Believe me, Great-Nephew, it was plain enough to see, the long string of beggars at every street corner, the fearful mortality that heaped the Norwich churchyards until they stood several feet higher than the surrounding roadways. But I owe the firmness of my opinions, and the constant utterance I made of them, not to any calculation of how or when they would become accepted . . .'

'Oh, I didn't suggest it . . .'

'I know that. But you will have difficulty in knowing how the reality of the Christian command, to love one's neighbour as oneself, was impressed on me, at least once a week and often by casual meetings with one who merited the halo of a saint far better than many of the semi-legendary characters that fill most calenders, and used to be commemorated on most of the days of the year . . .'

'I think I can guess . . .'

'You well may. For that learned and utterly unselfish

soul has his memorial stone, engraved with his name and dates, in the Meeting House where he ministered with such devotion that his tenure of the pulpit was all too short!'

'Dr. William Enfield,' I hastened to interpose.

'That is his name. It only shows how faulty are the measurements by which we judge the duration of events. Twelve brief years only sufficed for all that Almighty Providence gave him the power to say.'

'How right you are, Uncle. For William Enfield, you will like to know, has his name in the *Dictionary of National Biography*. There is a whole column about him, and a list of his works that runs to twelve bound volumes and publications of miscellaneous matter besides.'

'You astonish me, Nephew. Tell me more of this admirable public record . . .'

'It is all since your day, Uncle. But you are far too wise to accept the silly cynicism that says man is born, he suffers, and he dies . . .'

'It was all too true of the majority of the population . . .'

'I hope I can comfort you by pointing out that today any noteworthy character will have the dates during which he lived, and the works of which he was capable, inscribed and indexed.'

'As I said before, how truly admirable . . .'

'We need not lose ourselves too deeply in praise of what is, undoubtedly, a very useful publication. Veracity bids me, Great-Uncle, to point out that many of the names entered in the *Dictionary of National Biography*, even those which fill the larger number of columns, are concerned with people for whom you and I would have little admiration.'

'Alas, I fear that may be the case. But I will forgive a compilation a great deal if it rescues from the oblivion that I know all too well overtakes many who deserve memorials, in particular, such a character as Enfield was.'

'I can well believe it. His portrait, a mere photographic reproduction . . . if you know what I mean . . .'

'I have heard a good deal, and seen examples of this method of taking shadow pictures, or silhouettes, in the years during which I have been hanging on your walls, produced below my gaze . . .'

'That is, alas, the only common and worthless kind of record we possess of a very beautiful face. I use the word in the sense that sheer nobility of character shines through the mere structure of skin and bone, even in a photograph . . .'

'It was a reality to me, when he stood in the old pulpit, elevated above the heads of the rapt congregations!'

'Something of that implicit command lingers in the photographic reproduction.'

My great-uncle appeared to hesitate. Was it my fancy, or did his eyes turn inward upon himself, when he sought to recall the impressions of his time on earth? His voice seemed to reach me with an added sonorous note:

'I owe him more than I can say. Not only was he the mentor of my formative years, but he did so much to free the mind, especially the Dissenting and Non-Conformist mind, of the narrow tenacity forced on it, by the years of persecution. For men who are threatened, particularly on account of their religious belief, are driven in upon themselves, and tend to . . . shall I say, solidify, and may in fact become as intolerant, even bigoted, as the oppressors who caused the mischief.'

I listened to this with a certain sense of short-coming and hastened to reply:

'I must confess that I have read little of Dr. Enfield's works. Tell me, what especially striking . . .?'

'He showed so clearly that the intention that informs any action is as important as the action in itself. Hence the strict rule obtaining among Nonconformists and Dissenters that forbade them to take part in, or witness, theatrical performance he showed to be shortsighted and mistaken. He pointed out that to cut oneself off from the works of William Shakespeare and John Milton was not the way to direct appreciation of what is best in our language, or most moving...'

'Good old Enfield!' I could not help feeling a gust of warm approval for that figure which had, until that day, the rather pallid associations that seem natural when one is thinking of someone only known by reading his name on a memorial tablet in a place of worship. My uncle looked rather shocked. I saw in a moment that I had been guilty of a lapse of manners. Uncle had a reverence for the memory of the Reverend William Enfield that had been impressed upon him by that figure in life. I was casting about for some adequate form of apology for my vulgar and slangy expression. I failed to find it and was feeling rather compunctious. But my uncle, I hope from affection, but possibly also because of his shadowy constitution as a mere image on my wall, apparently forgave my indiscretion.

'Dr. Enfield not only gave us sermons in which the loftiest thought was conveyed with convincing eloquence. He was what his immortal forerunner, Dr. Taylor, described in the text of his first sermon, in that superb eight-sided Meeting House...'

'What was that?'

'Dr. Taylor proclaimed "... We are Christians, and simply Christians." Dr. Enfield, forty years later, exemplified that definition. He gave of his utmost. He summoned the boys of his congregation and acquaintance, to come to his house at six in the morning, and there he gave us the extra instruction that we were likely to miss in the normal education of most of us, directed as it necessarily was, to earning an honest living.'

'What did it consist of, at that early hour?'

'Latin and Greek, as our aptitude showed us capable of learning, and the translation of the authors of antiquity, the great poems and dramas.'

My great-uncle could almost be heard to heave a sigh. 'You call it that early hour. My recollection is that our minds were fresh from sleep. Those who seemed to find attendance at those early gatherings somewhat of a strain would be given a cup of milk by kindly Mrs. Enfield, so that they were able to gather full advantage of what her husband put at their disposal!'

'That was a sensible thought, and rather advanced for the period.' The word slipped out inadvertently. I did not mean to sound as though I underrated the achievement of the decade that was to be crowned at Trafalgar. But my uncle did not appear offended:

'They were, the Enfields, as you say, people of views well in advance of their time. Had he been spared, no doubt he would have played some part in the great movement towards Reform, that was to crown the years of peace. But he did not live to see the era of special betterment that slowly and painfully succeeded the half-century of war and revolution that my generation was called upon to support. It is much that while the Continent was racked with conquest and desolation I still retain, from the first half of my life on earth, an admiration for literature and drama that had no connection with my daily round of earning my living in my father's shop and later in my own. But that instruction he made available to me had a decisive effect upon the main event of my life. Whenever the plays of Shakespeare were being performed at the Theatre Royal, Dr. Enfield encouraged the boys under his influence to save their pennies and spend them in the cheap seats of the gallery.'

'Of course you were lucky, Uncle. You were able to witness the performances of Mrs. Siddons.'

'Ah, my boy,' something perhaps in the name awakened memories that led my great-uncle to a more familiar frame of mind than he normally exhibited, 'that was indeed a great occasion. That incomparable woman overcame the prejudices of the puritan section of Norwich. The Theatre Royal was crowded, people fought for seats even.'

'Do tell me, Great-Uncle, what was she like?'

He paused a moment, and then, evidently wishing to gratify my thirst to see, down the long vista of decades, a person and figure I could otherwise only know by description, continued:

'The plain answer is, she was like nothing but herself. I rather gather from what I have seen and heard, here, in your dining-room, that the conventions of stage representations have varied, naturally enough, since my day. She was taller than the average woman and carried herself with a conscious air, derived from being so long the centre of a thousand admiring glances. She had adopted, reasonably enough, a measured diction, calculated to reach the remotest seats in any house in which she was called upon to play. I think it is probable that, if it were possible to bring her to life, as I heard her, you, in the idiom of your time, might find her appearance and delivery stilted and artificial. I think in our day we rather expected that. To us, people who played on the stage so continuously every night of the week, and on many a matinée, were not expected, when they mixed with their public, in ordinary conversation, to become ordinary themselves. It was part of their professional equipment to be in themselves, something of what they portrayed on the boards. But her features were fine, she had retained a good colour, she was no plumper than a woman of her stature can well afford to be. Of course, she had her mannerisms, the downcast eye, raised when the direct glance gave support to the words of a sentence, the foot advanced, as though in private converse she was still before a row of footlights, and visible, as it were, from one side only, even when standing amid a group of people in commonplace, banal conversation.'

'You were fortunate, Uncle, to be granted admission to the social occasions in which such distinguished people were to be met.'

'Dr. Enfield had the entry of the best houses in the City. He was, you will have gathered, something of a notability himself. His congregation included Sir James Edward Smith, who brought the Linnean Collection from Sweden, at some personal risk. There was also Henry Reeve, the Clerk of the Privy Council, who generally spent his Sunday in Norwich. There were Sarah Austin and Mrs. Barbauld, and Amelia Opie. There was William Smith, who became our Member of Parliament. I saw a good deal of him, in later years, when he took part in the Anti-Slavery Movement . . .'

'You were privileged to mix in such circles . . .'

'There was nothing exclusive in Dr. Enfield's wide range of acquaintance and friends. The poorest boy who showed ability would be admitted to the little group that met before breakfast at his house. Some few did manage to take full advantage of the opportunity. They picked up manners above their station in life and learned to keep themselves respectable in appearance and speech. I always suspected that those who seemed to be without decent clothes, which was not unusual in those days, were helped by the Enfields with the outgrown suits of their own sons.'

'I suppose many did not have the chances you enjoyed of meeting Mrs. Siddons and members of the stock company at the Theatre Royal?'

'No, indeed. Money was not so plentiful as today as I gather from what I have heard in the conversations that have taken place before me, these many years. It was much for most of Dr. Enfield's boys, if they succeeded in earning the price of a place in the gallery of the Theatre. No seat was guaranteed up there.'

My great-uncle here relapsed into what, on his face in the portrait, can only have been a subdued chuckle. I waited, convinced that he was enjoying some memory that caused him amusement. He seemed to become aware that I was at a loss to follow him, and his explanation came muffled, as he reached back in his memory to times so long gone by.

'I can give you but a dim glimpse of what the audience in the gallery was like . . .'

In fact, I seemed to trace, on his features, signs of effort to reach out to me, and make me understand. 'Performances were long. Imagine an evening in which the main item was Congreve's *Way of the World*, followed by a farce *The Mock Doctor*, or *The Dumb Lady Cured*. These would be preceded by a prologue, and might be followed by items of the most miscellaneous description. Songs, solo dances, imitations of well-known characters and speeches advocating one or another of the political projects of the moment, paid for, no doubt, by one or another of the parties interested. The occupants of the gallery, who had struggled so hard

D

to find foothold, if no more was procurable, might well not have eaten since midday and would have provided themselves with something to allay hunger and thirst. It might be a pig's trotter and a pint of stout. And these ... er ... comestibles had a further advantage. When consumed, the hoof of the trotter, or the pewter mug, might be used to show disapproval of the piece being played, or dislike of one or other of the actors performing!'

'I suppose it added to the excitement. But the holders of the better seats below ...'

'They were helpless, Nephew. No, it was the unfortunate player who happened to be visible on the stage, at the moment, who had to distract the attention, or win applause from the more equable quarters of the house, and so keep up the continuity ...'

'But scenes of rowdiness cannot have taken place when anyone as celebrated as Mrs. Siddons ...'

'No, indeed, and there you have the measure of her ability. Tough and often drunken the occupants of the cheaper seats might be. But she had it in her to command attention. Even the semi-literate in the gallery, or the back of the pit, would be charmed into silence, and wide-eyed attention, when she, and the few who might be considered, if not her equals, at least worthy to take the other parts in the scenes she so easily dominated, were performing the better-liked of the popular successes of those days.'

'It must have been a hard life, Uncle, for the average actor and actress ...'

'Of course it was. One can hardly blame those who had not the ability to succeed, or the endurance not to succumb, if they gave way to the endless temptations that lay in wait for them at every turn. For the men there were drink and gambling, the one to provide at least temporary oblivion, the other the desperate chance of unexpected gain. For the woman there were the constant offers of those who posed, at least for the moment, as admirers, and whose promises, however seductive, a half-starved and ill-paid girl listened to if for no better reason than that they broke up the monotony, and overcame, even temporarily, the discomforts.'

'You went, though, with other thoughts in your minds.'

'We had been prepared by Dr. Enfield for the great speeches Mrs. Siddons, and other celebrated visitors to our Theatre Royal, made memorable, though the general level of the stock company's performances was high in those days. As I have said, it had to be. And there was a sense of freshness and determined effort, when, as was often the case, there were two or three plays presented in a week.'

'It makes one ache to think of the constant rehearsal necessary, and the mere learning of the parts that must have robbed many a member of the company of much-needed sleep.'

'Yes. Of course, the older hands must have had prodigious memories, and could no doubt call upon them, for the words of the more constantly repeated favourites. Again, there are some plays in which the dialogue gives easy and obvious cues. Sheridan's must have been a blessing, I often thought, not only for the easy naturalness of the lines, but from what was then a frequent source of comedy, the apeing of the manners of a small circle, which were intriguing to those to whom they were familiar in life, and laughable to those to whom they were remote, by their affectation and artificiality. *The School for Scandal* was played before us very shortly after its first appearance at Drury Lane, and repeatedly as its acceptability became obvious. So permanent members of the company did not have to do more than refresh their memories. Again, when *The*

Rivals was put on, think what a godsend a character like Sir Lucius O'Trigger was to the hard-working actor, in search of easily gained applause.'

'It must have been a relief after many a turgid "book" drawn from the older repertoire of Restoration.'

'Not only those. There was a feeling for translations of Molière, through which *Les Fourberies de Scapin* became *The Cheats of Scapin*.'

'Wasn't that rather strong meat for the provincial public gathered at the Theatre Royal?'

'Not when one reflects that in the cheaper seats there were not only idlers, officers of the garrison ogling the female players, but solid shopkeepers like my own parents, to whom an evening out at the Theatre was a rare treat, something that had to be enjoyed, because it must not, could not, be wasted. There were, besides, people like the Earl of Orford, in a position to demand performances of pieces he might have seen in London, and wished to see again. With him would be assembled the members of Dr. Enfield's congregation, and their friends and circle, like Amelia Opie, before her views became so strict. The varying tastes of the audience accounted for productions I have never heard mentioned in all the years I have hung here upon the walls of your room. I was quite astonished lately to hear one of your guests mention *Oedipus, King of Thebes*. The version we witnessed portrayed his marriage. But at least the authors of classical antiquity were not excluded. From them the range was wide. We might have *The Beaux' Stratagem* and *Love's Last Shift* to follow. And in order to comply with the rather shadowy regulation that drama should only be played as an adjunct to musical programmes we had such "Operas", as they were billed, as *The Devil to Pay*. Have you ever heard it?'

'No, indeed. Nor of it. What can it have been like!'

'That was not the point. It gave colour to the thin pretence that serious drama crept in, as it were, by virtue of the musical items it accompanied!'

'I see. Hence the term melodrama, I have been told, first indicated drama played along with and in between the musical items.'

'No doubt that was so. But those of us who owed our love of the Theatre to Dr. Enfield's teaching, of course, looked largely to Shakespeare. Ah, I recall now the appearance of Mrs. Siddons as Rosalind in *As You Like It* . . .'

My great-uncle's face seemed to recede as he recalled the enthusiasms of so many years ago. For a moment it reverted to the static quality of the portrait. Afraid that I might lose connection with his thoughts, I hastened to ask:

'I suppose the text used in those days was liable to all sorts of emendations and alterations. I know Cibber was guilty of taking every sort of licence with the words he and the company in which he played were to speak. I have even heard actors defend the practice on the grounds that Cibber knew by urgent experiment what lines would attract attention, and go over to the audience with effect . . .'

This query brought back the colour to my great-uncle's cheeks and the living spark to his eyes. Evidently I had touched a point that revivified his memories. 'From what I have heard, as I hang here, it seems likely that what I believe you call "publicity" was a very different thing in my day. It was at once naïve, and honest. It had to be. For the rougher elements of the theatre-going public were all too ready to resent, and visit their resentment at the next performance, if they felt they were being deceived. That accounts for a bill-posting I remember seeing announcing:

King Lear and His Three Daughters, written by Shakespeare and altered by Tate.'

Both of us joined in a smile at this confession.

'Then there was the announcement of *Macbeth*, with the added attraction: "during which Signor Rossignole from Naples would introduce his imitations of birds, from the Wren to the Raven".'

Here our intercourse was interrupted by the amusement this recollection occasioned him as much as it did me. But he had more to follow:

'There was also the same versatile Italian who put on: "A quartetto of his own composition, on a violin without any strings".'

Before I had done laughing, the train of thought I had set in motion reminded him to add:

'I seem to remember that the alterations made in *Macbeth* were made, it was announced, "to allay the fears of ladies who might be alarmed by the thunder and lightning in the play"!'

'Good gracious. Were the Noises Off so loud as all that?'

'I think we accepted them for what they were intended to convey. The ghost in *Hamlet* and the witches on the blasted heath were always very popular.'

'That I can understand, for in my childhood the best-attended sideshows of the great Easter Fair on the Cattle Market, and the slightly lesser one which was allowed at Christmas, were those of Pepper's Ghost. I suppose the name means nothing to you?'

'No, I think not. Of course, there was plenty of blatant superstition, avoidance of churchyards after dark, crossing of fingers, setting of one's shoes, when one discarded them at night, "one coming and one going" to avoid their appropriation by the Devil.'

'Yes, those are remembered today, if they have lost some of their original urgency!'

'There, again, you have the long-distance effect of the teaching of Dr. Enfield. He used to say: "There is a reasonable explanation for all the odd and queer events of life, though almighty Providence may not have thought fit to reveal it to us!"'

Here my great-uncle's face reflected something of the undying awe with which he regarded any of the pronouncements of his mentor. But it gradually faded and his features became lively again, as he was enabled by memory to relive his past.

'I had it handed down to me, Nephew, for I was a child at the time, that the opening of the Theatre Royal was serious enough. It had to be announced as "The Grand Concert Hall" and the players by virtue of an Act passed by Parliament in 1758 became His Majesty's Servants. The performances were announced as Concerts, and the plays, ostensibly given gratis between musical items, were trifles such as *Richard the Third*. But, in fact, Shakespeare was frequently played. Indeed I have seen an old bill of my father's, from which I remember that, on the opening night of the theatre which Thomas Ivory built, the curtain rose to soft music. At the Invocation of the leading player, the Shades of Shakespeare, as the "Genius of the Stage" appeared, and reclining on a pedestal, read the prologue from a roll of paper. Dr. Enfield later made me memorise the words as an exercise in dramatic diction. They have never left me and they ran like this:

'When first the Muses breathed Dramatic Lays
Their dress was rude, their Stage, the Public Ways,
Their song unpolished, dissonant and loud.

To catch the Attention of th' unpolished crowd;
But, tho' thus barbarous, rude, reformed and mean
Yet some were found to patronise 'em then
Some generous breasts, whose judgment could foresee
What the Young Art in length of time might be.
Then, like the Approaches of the Morning Light,
The stage improved, and by degrees grew bright
Because the Mirror, which displays the charms
Of Virtue, dressed in her more lovely forms,
Where erring mortals might distinctly see,
What they should not, and what they ought to be—
Hence Shakespeare, Jonson, Dryden chose the Stage
At once to please and to reform the Age;
The tender Passions of the Soul to move
And show the judgments due to perjured love;
To curb the wild Pursuits of thoughtless Youth
And gently lead 'em to the Paths of Truth;
To show that Merit, tho' distrest, may shine
(Distresses tend to prove it more Divine!)
That still, the Virtuous Man alone is great
Since Virtue only mocks the frowns of Fate.
In this we have assumed Theatric dress
And hence we drew out Prospect of Success;
Hence too, presume we boldly to appear
Before this Kind Assemblage circled here;
Who, many years have frank Indulgence shown,
And deigned to call this company their own;
Which favour, still we struggle to preserve,
Ne'er from the path of Grateful Duty swerve
But toil in cheerful Heart and willing nerve.
May Peace and Plenty through this City flow
And all the blessings Future can bestow;
Sick Trade revive, and drooping Commerce smile,

Commerce the boast and Blessing of our Isle!
This ample fabric, raised at large expense
We hope will meet with ample Recompence;
Or else (as Archer says) did fair machine
Fall, like the Eddystone, at once, souse in.
But that's needless fear—you'll ne'er allow
Us to be sufferers for pleasing you.
No Garricks, Barrys, we pretend to be,
Such we presume, you'll not expect to see;
Nor search for Cibber, Pritchard or yet Bellamy—
For our whole Corps this short conclusion draws,
Our end is gained, in gaining your Applause:
Indulged with which no study will seem hard,
Your servants we, and You our special Guest.
Be it our sphere to Labour, Yours to Reward.'

'Really, Uncle, are you able to retain a body of lines like that for so long?'

'You'll find, my boy, that, as one ages, long-past events, words spoken years ago, come more easily to the memory than more recent ones. And, as I have said, since those lines were admired by Dr. Enfield, and given me to learn, they have been impressed on a memory that is now more retentive of what was once important and less sensitive to more recent impressions!'

'It must have been a memorable scene, indeed, that opening night!'

'I have gathered, during the years I have hung here, that there has been a vast increase in the means of entertainment. In my day there was only the Theatre Royal for the half of the year when leisure was only possible after it became dark. Even in the evenings of spring and summer there was little alternative save an excursion, if the weather permitted, in one of the public gardens that adjoined the City gates.'

'Oh, nowadays, as you have seen and heard, there are all kinds of mechanical means of reproducing music, the human voice and less articulate sound. You hear me turn a knob, on that glass-faced box there, and as you listen there come the reports of the weather, the announcement of the hours and, between news summaries, what is called the broadcasting of plays, lectures, accounts of foreign travel and notable events, even games . . .'

'Dear me, how very ingenious. Yes indeed, I have learned to connect the sound of voices, which I could not otherwise account for, even when no one was present in the room, with that box. Your hearing must become very fatigued, Great-Nephew!'

'At times we feel it is, perhaps. But, after all, by turning the knobs on that box we have considerable powers of selection from several "programmes", as they are called. Finally one can always turn the second knob, and shut off the artificial sounds altogether.'

'That must be a rare relief at times. Indeed, a necessity if you are to have peaceful sleep at night. We had, of course, our news-sheet, which did keep us informed of important events, with a certain delay. But music had to be performed by those skilled in it, and the drama, as I have told you, was only possible in a building erected for the purpose, used at known hours, and accessible by payment at the door, or purchase of a ticket beforehand. So I learned from Dr. En- field a respect for the proper delivery of the more admired of the great speeches of our authors. And it led on to the most important event of my life.'

The deeply moved tone in which the sentence ended seemed to demand response.

'You mean, your meeting with Miss Goddard!'

'Yes, of course!'

There fell a silence so complete that I began to fear that the depth of emotion which, I assumed, he must still feel for the central and tragic episode that had brought us together, might render him unwilling to continue his curious interchanges with me. Instead of words, there seemed to come from the portrait a sigh so prolonged, so mournful, that I held my tongue, forbidden to intrude on his feelings.

However, it ended, and when I ventured to raise my eyes to his likeness, the handsome benevolent face, of past middle life, looked just as it always had, dignified, but friendly and above all accessible. In the hope that I might renew our interchange and also possibly that he might find relief, as some do in giving expression to a deep-rooted wound, I ventured:

'You saw her first, at the Theatre!'

Once again, a great sigh intervened. But this time it was not merely reminiscent of mortal loss, but rather as if he were gathering his faculties. Presently he seemed to succeed and I thought I heard the words:

'Not at the Theatre here, in our native town.'

The old voice seemed to strengthen. Perhaps he was not unwilling to tell the intimate story of his life to one of his own blood, who was so anxious to learn at first hand (if that is how our interview was to be regarded) that deeply moving recital.

'You must know that I became dissatisfied with my father's trade of glover. I cannot tell why, save that I think I derived, from Dr. Enfield's teaching, an urge for more knowledge and wider experience. Also his insistence on sheer value, that life was not merely a matter of eating and drinking, sleeping and working. That value was irrespective of bulk, that gold and jewels, which so often were mentioned in his discourse from the pulpit, and his reading of lessons from Holy Writ, may have led me to give increased attention to the hands I saw exhibited in my father's glove shop. Thus I became attracted to the fineness and good keeping, and above all to the rings I saw discarded by customers trying on gloves. So, with my parents' permission, I applied to Mr. Dunham, to be admitted a partner with him in his goldsmith and jewellery business, on the Gentleman's Walk. Mr. Dunham replied that I must first get some instruction in the business, and that as he had no time to teach me, while conducting his affairs, I had better spend a year, at least, in London, to obtain knowledge of how precious metals and choice stones were dealt with. He advised me to write to the firm Mr. Vineyard Perkins Partners, of Dorset Square, London, and they very obligingly expressed their willingness to allow me to assist in their business, on terms that my parents were able to agree to.

'So I left my native city, by the mail coach which ran in those days from the Norfolk Hotel to the Swan with Two Necks in Lad Lane. The journey took the whole night, with halts at regular stages, such as Long Stratton, Scole, Stonham and Ipswich . . .'

'I suppose you were able to get some sleep, when the coach stopped to change horses.'

'It was the spring of the year, but the nights were still cold. I have a recollection that I began to find my feet becoming numb, until they had no more sensation than lumps of ice. But at Ipswich there was some little delay for the delivery and receipt of mail and parcels and by stamping on the ground, and running up and down the inn yard, one restored the circulation. The travellers who could afford to do so treated themselves to hot brandy and water, but the provision my parents had made did not admit of luxuries for me.'

'Great-Uncle, you must have been nearly frozen in an outside seat on so long a journey!'

'In those days we were accustomed to a degree of discomfort that, I gather from what I have heard in your room, would have been deeply resented nowadays. But a journey such as I made, my longest to that date, was exciting, and the prospect filled me with anticipation.'

'It must have done!'

'I little realised to what I was trundling, behind those trotting horses, or in what way my journey would make a permanent mark on my life!'

'You had never before traversed the Essex countryside by Epping and Burnham Beeches. Was it getting light!'

'My recollection is, that I was so sound asleep that I had to be roused when we reached our destination. The first thing I knew was that my fellow passenger, against whom I had been leaning, had to shake me, to secure his own release from my weight, which in those days was fortunately not great. He was a bagman, as they were called, on his way to sell the products of the Bolingbroke firm I was destined to come to know so well. Once he had left me, I descended from my seat, in busy London. I recall even now the stiffness of my limbs, and my bewilderment at the noise and bustle, like all the Norwich market days in a year rolled into one. Jostled and pushed, I made my way out into the thronged and muddy streets, where the concourse of traffic, at eight in the morning, was a menace to one's safety, and the splashing of dirt from the roadways a disfigurement to one's apparel. It was some time before I could attract the attention of a passer-by, to ask my way to Brick Lane, where

I had lodgings engaged for me. Indeed I should not have succeeded in finding my way had I not found an individual who seemed to be at his leisure. He was willing enough to show me the way, but when we reached the address and I thanked him, he said:

' "I generally charges eightpence for that!"

'To this I demurred, whereat he attempted to snatch my bag and would have made off with it, doubtless, but I had turned the straps round my wrist, and was able to defeat his manœuvre. Upon which he made off before the good people who were to receive me had opened the door.

'I was made welcome, for they were servants of the neighbouring Truman's Brewery and Quaker folk, acquainted with members of the Norwich Meeting. I told them how I had arrived at their door, and of the request made by my guide. They explained:

' "He asked for eightpence, hoping that you had only silver on you. Had that been the case, he would have offered to get change, and you would never have seen him again . . ."

'Such was my introduction to the habits and inhabitants of London. Otherwise, my friends were good to me and I became so interested in my professional experience that I never regretted having to make my way in London.'

'You found your duties interesting and not too strenuous?'

'The hours were long, but my contacts with the public were interesting. Though the shop remained open as long as anyone required to make purchases, the method of weighing, sorting and pricing of the goods for sale was enthralling. We only dealt with those sufficiently affluent to be seeking the valuable wares the firm had to dispose of . . .'

'But you must have needed a good deal of teaching, and

I suppose there were risks in handling the costly goods you were learning to deal with?'

'As to that, I found that there was another assistant, a pleasant youth named Pooley. He was a year older than I and had been employed in the shop for even longer. It fell to him, more often than to the fully occupied heads of the business, to show me what he had recently learned. The commerce of the house flourished, based on the good name of the proprietors, and Pooley and I had few idle moments!'

'There must have been risks connected with a trade in merchandise of high intrinsic value.'

'There were. But the long knowledge the head of the firm had acquired enabled them to form a rapid and sound opinion of those with whom they had to deal. I recall a very plausible and well-dressed gentleman who brought in a young lady ... at least she had the looks and the innocent way of speaking of one such ... Various trinkets and ornaments were asked for and she expressed admiration and delight. The person by whom she was accompanied suggested that she tried on a necklace and some ear-rings and, at this, Pooley gave a sharp tug at my coat-tails, and I obediently followed him to the door, where we stationed ourselves. When this was observed, the intending customers soon began to criticise the objects she was wearing and she was offered others. This led to her discarding those she had essayed, and, shortly, she and her accomplice, as I have no doubt he was in fact, made some excuse and prepared to leave. Then I heard the jeweller say politely:

' "You have left your necklace, madam, here it is. Will you kindly hand me back the one you have in your muff?" There were apologies and laughter from her companion, but Pooley explained this attempt to exchange a worthless article for one of some great value. . . .'

'You had to be prepared for every sort of trickery.'

'Not always, of course. There were genuine enough cases of pitiable distress. Widows of officers engaged in the fighting then taking place in remote parts of the world. There were decently honest folk reduced to penury by the wars, or some other less-explicable misfortune. Then there were also perfectly honest and well-meaning members of aristocratic, or landowning families, who had to be allowed long credits to find the funds for the purchases they had made.

'Of course, it was a time of disturbance and political uncertainty and the future was often in doubt. Then there were genuinely honest and affluent folk, able to pay for what they required. It was in connection with one of these latter that the far-reaching designs of Providence brought me into contact with the person I shall always regard as the supreme attachment of my life.'

The old voice ceased. The features in the portrait seemed invested with a tender melancholy I at once understood and which forbade me to offer remark or make inquiry that might have seemed impertinent. Slowly life filtered back to the face. The lips seemed as if they moved, or was it just staring at them?

'One day,' I thought I heard, 'Pooley said to me: "I have to deliver a parcel at Drury Lane Theatre. Sometimes the doorkeeper is friendly and lets me into the audience. Would you like to come with me?"

'I told him how Dr. Enfield's teaching had given me so great an admiration for the Drama, and arranged to accompany him. He seemed amused rather than interested by what I could tell him of the Theatre Royal in Norwich.

' "Ah, my boy," he asserted, "but this is Drury Lane, the premier house in the kingdom. Mrs. Siddons and the heads of the profession do not visit here. They play for seasons."

'I did not argue this point, but readily went with him, pushing through the London crowd which was besieging the entrance to the Theatre, and was led by back alleys of a most poverty-stricken and dissolute appearance to the stage door, where a savage and irascible doorkeeper at first bade me keep away, but on hearing the name of our firm, and that of the performer to whom we had to make delivery, he relented:

' "Does it take two of you?" he grudgingly demanded.

' "My companion is with me for greater security," replied Pooley. "We are the bearers of valuable goods!"

'With this assurance the fellow seemed content, and we were allowed to pass. Can you imagine the scene which met our eyes, Nephew?'

'Only be hearsay and report. I have been "behind", as it is still called, but the conditions must be very different.'

'I shall never forget that first visit I paid with Pooley. We penetrated a series of passages, the dirt and confused traffic in which were unbelievable. We emerged into a queer world of scenery and properties in which landscapes and buildings were standing at all angles and positions, amid ladders, ropes and objects of which I, at least, could not determine the use. The people of this unreal world had an air of listless excitement, the men and boys in queer undress, and the ladies treating us with brilliant smiles and welcoming gestures, until they learned our business was not with them. At length we penetrated to a row of doors and Pooley knocked on the one to which we had been directed. It was opened by a slatternly and unprepossessing female, a little way, while she learned our errand which she repeated over her shoulder.

E

' "Let them approach!" came the reply in a high stilted voice, and room was made for us in a confined cabin ... the word describes the air its restricted dimensions had, like those on board ship. There, before a bedaubed and mended mirror, the frame of which was stuck full of cards and scraps of paper, bearing dates, information and detail which I was unable to decipher, sat a person engaged in completing her "make-up". That is to say, she was at once a woman of easy address and cheerful manner, who seized the parcel we conveyed and handed it to her attendant to be opened. This allowed her to complete the disguise she was assuming. While treating us to brilliant glances and grateful words, interrupted by searching questions as to what her "dresser" was revealing, she became before our eyes, and with a lack of concealment that to me, at least, was embarrassing, to assume the character she was to portray at the performance shortly to begin. However, she appeared grateful enough and even spared moments from her preoccupation with the curiously exaggerated face and figure she was improving on her natural lineaments. This was cut short by a peremptory knock on the door:

' "Beginners!" proclaimed a voice that from its sonorous warning note might as well have uttered "Condemned" or "Indicted".

' "Lord save us!" she ejaculated. "Kippens!" (this was addressed to her companion) "take these young gentlemen and tell Northgate to let 'em into the Pit."

'This sentence, which might have been an invitation to descend into the infernal regions, resulted in the harridan behind her ushering us out with no particular favour and hurrying us along yet another passage, until we came to a dilapidated door, at the foot of some steps, guarded by a kind of "turnkey" who regarded us with sardonic amusement through his one eye.

'However, he obeyed the message sent him, and allowed us to penetrate into the crowded passage that in those days surrounded the back of the Pit. This, frequented by sellers of oranges, bills of the performance and other matter, allowed us to find a couple of vacant seats in an obscure corner, in which we could see little of the stage, but hear tolerably well, as the curtain shortly rose on the piece selected for performance that night.'

At this point, my great-uncle's face seemed to regain its usual impassivity. I had no clue as to why this should be. Can portrayals of those long dead suffer from fatigue when struggling to make themselves informative to their descendants, who may, from time to time, interrogate their unchanging demeanour? I don't know.

3

The London Apprentice

WHEN one holds a prolonged mental colloquy (if that is what it was) with a portrait of an ancestor, one is subject to limitations. There he hangs, as he appeared when he sat, in his sixties, to be painted. I do not know the exact date, but he had been Sheriff of the City in 1805, and Mayor in 1819. His ultimate honours, his knighthood and second mayoralty, were still to come. He was already a public character, had already addressed a meeting on the subject of Peace and against the Property Tax. It may very well have been that amid the general rejoicing at the end of forty years of almost continuous warfare his relatives persuaded him to be 'done, in oils'. He looks about sixty, and his sister, who by then had her family of thirteen children, and had lost five of them, was portrayed by the same artist, as was her husband, also. So I fancy they 'made a job of the three of them', and I would like to be told if William Hilton, the painter, reduced his charge for the triple commission. I should not be surprised to find that it was the wealthy bachelor Uncle Yallop who paid. He has a look of modest, if conscious, worth that may have arisen from that fact, or may of course be the result of the honours that were already accumulating on his shoulders.

So let us call him sixty years old. But I had become familiar with some details of his youth, up to his sojourn in London that was to leave such a mark on his life. And when I next had leisure to sit down before the picture, and let myself go into that odd state of communion with him, I wanted to know more about his apprenticeship to the trade he had practised so successfully. At least, that is what I think he liked to call it, though he was not formally bound by any deed for a length of years, nor did he or his parents pay any premium so far as I have been able to learn.

Then I did have a stroke of luck that helped me to see what young Harrison Yallop was like, when his fellow apprentice first took him 'behind' the scenes, to deliver a parcel to a lady playing at Drury Lane. Among other family relics I turned up a miniature made of him about that time. I think I know why. The question formed in my mind : 'Did you ever think that the small oval portrait that was made of you would be treasured more than a century later, and might help to make your portrait speak to anyone of your blood?'

At first I thought I had made some stupid 'gaffe' and offended him. For as I sat there, with the miniature in my hand, tracing the plain resemblance of the full young face, all innocence and surprise at the world being the place he was discovering it to be, and not at all the place Dr. Enfield's teaching had taught him it ought to be, the larger full portrait made no sign. It remained just a thing of paint on canvas, and it was some moments before I felt that this must be so. The expression was deliberately assumed to mask the emotion I had unwittingly aroused. It was some time before I was able to feel that he was willing to reopen the old old wound and give me a glimpse of the long desperate losing battle of which the miniature was the memorial, and at length I became conscious that he was making me aware of the origin of the small smooth object I held in my hand.

'It was done to please her,' the words appeared to be wrung from him. 'I thought, years later, that the miniature at which you are now looking and a companion one, of which I will tell you, were the first signs that she realised, all too vividly, that we were never to be united in the holy bonds for which we were so deeply and seriously committed.'

'Did she, then, have a companion miniature made for you?'

'Yes, she did!'

He told me where it was to be found, but I was loth to press him, for I had a sense that I was touching him at a spot at which sensation had never been entirely calloused over, and that he still felt the bitter pangs of his long battle to try to preserve the life that was so precious to him. Then gradually he mastered those old, old emotions and eventually lent himself to account for the first gleam of that passion that was to be so amply reciprocated and to mark so deeply his life.

'We none of us ever fathom, Nephew, not merely the designs of Providence, but the odd and sometimes apparently irrelevant means of which it avails itself, to compass its ends. Who, that knew him, would ever have supposed that my colleague Pooley and his loose and irresponsible nature would bring me into intimacy with one so completely beyond his knowledge and foreign to his style of acquaintance?

'For Pooley soon began inviting me to go with him to Drury Lane, even when he had no parcel to deliver there. I think he felt that I lent him courage that he otherwise lacked, for the doorkeeper of the stage entrance, Northgate, was a fierce old man, by nature and by avocation. Many a silver coin Pooley must have passed him, and grudgingly he allowed us, on some flimsy excuse that Pooley proffered for our presence, that cannot have been believed.

'I soon found out the real motive of these visits. Pooley had become attracted by a young actress called Selina Lydgate. I could not altogether blame him. She was good-looking enough, and conscious of it, and used every means of her art to display her charms as the meagre opportunities of the commerce of backstage acquaintance allowed.' The voice of my uncle seemed to increase in volume, and deepen in tone, as if he were treading again those scenery-and-property-encumbered alleys and passages that were to lead to the meeting that was to mark so deeply the middle and end of his life.

'I will not blame Selina, if she let young Pooley hope for a degree of enjoyment of her favours, she had no real intention of according. To a girl in her situation there is no time to be lost, never can advantage be missed. Once or twice I saw plainly enough that he was by no means her sole admirer. Sometimes it was the doorkeeper who would oppose our entry.

' "Miss Lydgate ain't here tonight."

'Then, as we were turning away, Pooley disconsolate and unbelieving, we might catch sight of a couple descending from a private conveyance, or hackney coach, and hurrying to that obscure doorway and disappearing, with apparently no opposition from the doorkeeper. I would try to persuade Pooley to return home, even to the point at which he vented on me his natural resentment at the treatment he was receiving from her.

'However, we avoided any serious quarrel, which might have been unpleasant, when we were bound to meet and work together all day long. But Selina was as yet either not sufficiently practised in the goings and comings of chance encounters, or she may have been shrewd enough to fancy that young Pooley might, with his solid middle-class background like my own, provide her a more permanent status than her other suitors, even to the length of an offer of marriage. Pooley was either bemused enough to think this a possibility or dishonest enough to keep the prospect dangling before the girl as a means of retaining her attention.

'Months passed. I was engrossed in the business of which I was trying to master all the details, and if I was willing to accompany Pooley on his frequent evening excursions it was partly from the devotion to the theatre I had learned from Dr. Enfield, and partly mere friendliness, for there was not much else for a young man to do, other than sit in a tavern, or even a place of less-savoury repute, as many did, to their detriment. But as the evenings grew lighter, and the weather improved with the advancing season, Pooley said to me one day:

' "I've invited Selina to Ranelagh for the afternoon. Would you like to join us? She'll bring a friend!"

'Here he indulged in a wink and a leer, which ill became him. For he was not the sort of young man to whom a normal and honest glance is sufficient and who has to make falsely clear his meaning by all sorts of grimaces. I was not overjoyed by the invitation, but it was better than spending the daylight hours studying the manual and tables of weights, fineness and value of my profession in my lodgings, which, though comfortable enough, were in a narrow and overshadowed byway like Brick Lane. So I consented, and met Pooley by arrangement. He had hired a coach, which I thought a ridiculous extravagance, but that was not my business. We had not far to go, to pick up Selina and her friend, who answered to the name of Olivia. I was in doubt as to whether she could have been so christened, but it was probably assumed together with the languishing look she bestowed on me. I accepted the position for which I was obviously destined, namely to be her cavalier, and so allow Pooley to monopolise Selina, and add the respectable appearance of a *parti-carré* to two girls who preferred not to be seen at Ranelagh alone. They awaited us at a corner, which, I suspected, had been choosen so as not to reveal the poverty of the lodgings in which so many of such girls were condemned to exist.

'Off we set, clattering over the cobbles. I have heard in your room enough to know what a crude and primitive ride such people as we were, found within their means at that date. We arrived at the gardens, and Pooley not only paid off the coach, but found the entrance fees, in which I felt bound to join him, in shares. Well, the weather was fine, the fresh air a great treat, and the girls were good-natured. There was a Grand Operatic Concert, which they soon found dull and, with some hinting, proposed we should join the dancers who were going through the more popular exercises. This I declined to join, and offered, as my share of the entertainment, tea and the light viands which were all, I had learned, that performing members of a company permitted themselves at that hour.

'I did my best to be companionable to the young woman Olivia, but my interest in the drama I soon found was of an entirely different nature to her professional outlook. I ventured to remark:

' "How wonderfully Mrs. Siddons delivers those great speeches," referring to the current production at the Theatre.

' "Yes, indeed," was the reply: "She has a benefit on

Saturday, which may well amount to five hundred pounds."

' "The modulation of her voice . . ." I was about to continue . . .

'But I found the young woman was exchanging glances with a young officer in uniform, and was plainly more interested in gaining his attention than in discussing the art of which she was, if only a junior member, at least a practising one. I would willingly enough have abandoned her to find what entertainment she might with more congenial companions, but felt it my duty to Pooley to bear my part of the excursion he had arranged. So I continued in the strain of conversation that I supposed must interest her.

' "You must have played a variety of parts," I seem to recollect asking. But this was not a fortunate opening:

' "I've only been on the boards for three years," was the reply, in a rather chilly tone. "How old do you . . .?"

' "But I expect you will soon be asked to take some of the most important rôles," I put forward, in the hope that this would be more agreeably received.

' "The manager has promised me . . ." here she mentioned a character in some play of which the name conveyed nothing to me. I asked the name of the author, to which she answered:

' "Oh, you know. The piece they took over from the Garden."

'I may have looked mystified, for she added, for my comprehension, "Covent Garden."

' "What part does he intend to offer?" I inquired.

' "Oh, Dulcibella, of course. I shouldn't accept any other!"

'This information was proffered in a tone which led me to wonder if the manager would be equally certain to offer what I gathered must be regarded as one of the principal parts, to a young woman who admitted to no long experience in filling them.

' "Will that involve the learning of a fresh set of lines?"

' "That is part of the task."

' "Tell me," I inquired, "do you have to memorise the lines the other characters are saying?"

' "You have to know your cue!"

' "I have often wondered what happens when some other player forgets, or pronounces words you are not expecting?"

' "One has to pad out, and fill in and keep the scene moving."

' "Yes, so I have noticed!" I hoped that showed interest in her work, but she gave me a look as she should say "You know too much". She seemed little inclined to give away further information about her career, and turned the conversation towards my own work at the shop, how long I had known Pooley, and what were my favourite entertainments. I explained that I came up from the provinces, from a city in which we had a Theatre Royal, occupied by a stock company of very high standards. This seemed to interest her, for she asked:

' "Have you any influence with this Mr. John Brunton, at your theatre?"

'I had to confess that while I knew him well enough by sight, it was unlikely that he would know me better than as a face he might have glimpsed among those applying for seats.

' "Or," I added, "he may have seen me in company with Dr. Enfield when he devoted a Benefit to the funds of the Sunday Schools."

'This seemed to amuse her.

' "The manager at the Lane is not often inclined to give

Benefits for religious causes!" she giggled.

'"Beyond that Mr. Brunton will hardly know of my existence, though my parents are settled citizens of the City."

'"Who is this Dr. Enfield?"

'"A very learned and deeply read clergyman who gave me my first interest in the Drama!"

'She smiled and turned her head, and was soon engrossed in the antics of a young man who was mimicking the gestures and facial expressions of one of the members of the orchestra, performing in the "Hall of Melody", before which we were passing. Using his cane as a flute, he was entertaining his companions, all of whom seemed to me to have been well supplied with the negus on sale at the table, weak though I knew it to be. She did not conceal sufficiently her interest in this performance, and one of the hobbledehoys of the merry party began to address his remarks to her. To my astonishment, she did not seem in the least insulted; and while she did not reply to his overtures, she smiled and nodded and showed no unwillingness. As he made to approach her, however, she drew back, laughing, and slipped her arm through mine, spoke aside.

'"We must find Francis and Selina. It is near time we were going to the Theatre, and there are fines for those who are late."

'Thus appealed to, I reinforced the protection which my arm gave her by folding hers more firmly in mine, and, adjusting my grip of my own cane, in case it might be needed, I warned the fellow:

'"Keep your distance or it will be the worse for you." Rather to my relief, this firm front seemed to have the effect I intended. He drew back a yard or so, and demanded of his associates:

'"I wasn't doing nothing, was I?"

'These persons did not seem inclined to take his part, and his protestations only received the amusement they merited. Some gave him jeering encouragement, others taunts. I turned Olivia vigorously away from this unwelcome clamour, and, at some short distance, we were able to find Pooley and Selina.

' "Oh! there you are," exclaimed the latter, as if it had been our fault that they had engaged in dancing: "It is high time we were thinking of returning, Olivia. I am sorry to drag you from the delightful companionship I am sure you have so much enjoyed, Mr. Yallop!"

'Here the two young women burst into peals of what I thought to be ill-mannered and derisive laughter. Pooley drew us all towards the entrance, and engaged one of the hackney coaches there. As we rattled over the cobbles theatreward, Selina was at some pains to show gratitude for the entertainment he had provided and added archly:

' "Olivia has made quite a conquest, I am sure. Mr. Yallop will be anxious to know when she has a free afternoon that she can place at his disposal!"

'This again seemed to afford the young women the greatest possible amusement, in which Pooley made some effort to join. It must have been plain to him that I was not at all eager to seize the opportunity offered, but for the sake of good fellowship, and gaining approval of his inamorata, he managed to respond:

' "Mr. Yallop will be delighted, I'm sure. He is a great admirer of the fair sex, and a frequent attendant at your performances!"

'The young women were all smiles at this announcement, and Selina took the chance to rally me:

' "You will have to give her a wide choice of dates, Mr.

Yallop! She has a good many afternoons when she is not free!"

'This statement, again, appeared to give them both the liveliest satisfaction, and they laughed loud and long. However, when we reached the stage door, and took our leave, Olivia pressed my hand and thanked me for my companionship with the most winning grace. She even added:

' "Thank you also for being my champion against those roughs. One does make such unpleasant encounters in the public gardens. I am most grateful to you for having saved me from any further annoyance. Goodbye for now!"

'They disappeared with smiles and backward glances, Pooley discharged the coach, and we turned in the direction of our lodgings.

' "You're quite a cavalier!" he rallied me. "I expect you'll be the squire of many a dame, when you get over that shy, provincial manner of yours. It doesn't keep pace with the ways of the young town bloods. But cheer up, you'll improve, no doubt. I'll stand your friend!"

'What could I do but thank him?'

The voice had been droning on in my ears. Sometimes I closed my eyes, as one does when one needs to concentrate all one's wits on the hearing faculties. When I opened them again, there, on the wall, hung the portrait, and I thought I descried a change of expression. This could only be fancy, or at most a trick of the light, for the actual features had been fixed when William Hilton drew his brush over the canvas to portray them. Yet it seemed that there was a faint disorder, a look as of strain, as if my uncle were trying to convey to me more than a portrait a century and a half old can convey. At the same time, some such emotion (if a portrait can have emotion) seemed to lay bare the long, long vista down which its subject must be wistfully gazing at the life it had once lived on earth. Feeling a little compunctious, if I were indeed asking too much, and making demands that a painting cannot actually satisfy, I sought to make amends.

'Uncle, what a wonderful picture you have drawn for me of the daily life of a young assistant jeweller in the reign of George III . . .!'

I fancied I saw some softening and relaxation of the expression of the face, and hastened to increase it: "So that's what the young fellows did with their afternoon off. Of course you had been brought up more intelligently than young Poolcy, who seems to have had, as we should say, more money than sense. I gather that his parents allowed him some pocket money or he would not have been able to lavish such generosity on his friends and the friend of his young flame. I can quite understand that the way of passing the time, and the conversation, were a burden and a bore to you. But at least he was the means of procuring access to the theatre, and you did have the benefit of seeing some of the foremost of the stage figures of that time and witnessing performances that Dr. Enfield would have delighted in. But how did you prevent young Pooley from taking up your time with the sort of frivolity that went on at Ranelagh?'

Once again the face in the portrait seemed to soften, and be willing to communicate with me.

'On some occasions.' I felt rather than heard the spirit that had once lent light and feeling to those fine eyes. 'He made no propositions for sharing all our afternoons off. Our employers were kindly enough. I know that nowadays young people employed in what I have heard, during conversations in your room, described as the "distributing" trades, have regular holidays. Of course, we had not. Christmas Day and such of the religious festivals as Good Friday were observed. Even the clerks in the Bank of England were only allowed certain Saints' days in the year, which were selected for the most various reason and nearly always fixed long before in a most arbitrary manner. For us, it was a matter of one of the partners saying: "You young men had better take the afternoon for a walk over Hampstead Heath . . ." (or it may have been along the river to Westminster). If, again, it was a dull inclement day, we might be sent to survey the Regalia in the Jewel House at the Tower of London. Or even to watch handicraftsmen and their apprentices at work in the low dark back apartments of Hatton Garden and St. Bartholomew's from which so much of the valuable merchandise we handled in the shop came as it was refined, assayed, made up, repaired or altered. So the sort of invitation Pooley had thrown out, to take his Selina and her friend Olivia to Ranelagh, did not often recur. I made no advances. I had some few friends at whose houses I knew I should be welcome. On some days I would take a trip down or up river, with a waterman, to survey the forest of masts, the serried ranks of sea-going craft in the Pool, or above the Bridge. But I never knew if the rare occasions when Pooley invited me to join him were prompted by the fickle Selina's delight . . . and perhaps her deliberate policy . . . in keeping him dangling, and never letting him know precisely when her denial of her company was unavoidable, owing to rehearsal, or other professional engagement, and when it was because she had some other admirer whose attentions were more pressing, and whose resources afforded her more advantage. Sometimes he seemed, when we had an afternoon free, to be in very low spirits. At other times he conveyed by a series of winks and grimaces that he was anticipating goodness knows what unspecified delights. He was not vicious, like many another young fellow in those days of limited instruction and indifferent variety of entertainment for leisure. I grew conscious that his good or ill fortune, as he felt it, was often expressed by the noisy vigour, or the halting reluctance with which he put up the shutters, before the windows of the shop. This was a duty we shared, and when, sometimes, he asked me to relieve him of it, I gathered that he had made, or hoped for, an assignation at Drury Lane. On others, he slammed the heavy wooden boards into their place with a violence that I thought might be an expression of disappointment or chagrin. But I never knew. And it was through so uncertain and unpredictable a companionship that I came to have a preoccupation, that might seem similar to that which governed his temper and spirits, but which was, you will believe, so utterly different in essentials. It happened when he had invited me to go to the Lane on one of his happier evenings:

' "They are putting on *The Confederacy,* and for the burlesque a piece called *No Song No Supper.* I have no doubt that they will entertain you. I have other matters in hand!" He added this with an intriguing smile which made me sure that he not only looked forward to enjoying the company of Selina, when she was available, but liked me to be a witness of the fact, so as to present himself as the favoured suitor instead of the avoided and perhaps deceived and discarded third party as I feared he sometimes was. I did not tell him that I would much rather have had an entry to a Shakespeare drama, or even so light a comedy as *She Stoops to Conquer*!

' "What's more, my boy," he told me jovially, "I have the entry for the two of us tonight. So you'll be able to get a seat in the corner of the Pit. I've sweetened up the doorkeeper. And if you don't find any superior attraction be-

F

hind . . ." Here he treated me to one of his worldly wise and would-be humorous grimaces, "your evening won't be entirely wasted." '

The voice paused. Once more, there was a long, heart-rending sigh. Then the recital continued as I shut my eyes and made myself accessible:

'That it should have been Pooley, on that otherwise routine night of the year, that made me this offer and induced all that was to result from it, is one of those curious maladjustments through which Almighty Providence produces such utterly unforeseen effects!

'I can hardly speak of it, even now, without feeling emotion strong enough to disrupt this canvas, in which I now have my visible existence. It happened thus, Nephew:

'Pooley and I entered those grimy passages, behind the scenes, filled with the queer intermittent and indeterminate traffic of such a place, composed of those about to perform, always late, always in a state of emergency, and the steady laconic other race of dressers and stage hands, with their air of having survived ever greater crises. There would be also some few wealthy and well-dressed men, whose expression varied between illicit watchfulness to desperate alternations of hope and fear. Pooley had secured the admission to the auditorium for me and was just departing to whatever appointment he had secured, or thought he had, when, as I turned, I found myself facing two female figures, which had just entered. The taller, and more commanding, wore a rather forbidding expression on features that had been handsome, but carried herself with great assurance.

'But the other! Nephew, at the length of all those years of living with the memory of that encounter, I fail to convey what I felt. I had but a moment to catch a glimpse of the dark eyes that flashed an instant and answering message to mine. It was quite involuntary. I do not know if the generation to which you belong admits without a smile the description given so often in my day. Do the words "Love at first sight" sound credible?'

'Oh yes, Uncle. They are credible enough. We see no reason why such a moment of mutual sudden recognition should not occur.' I hastened to reassure him, lest I broke the fragile bridge of sentimental affection that was all we had, to enable me to receive the thoughts and feelings of my long-dead ancestor. 'But you will have gathered,' I went on, 'by your long experience of the verbiage used by my generation and the next, that the phrase may well be thought a cliché, and qualified as sentimental. You have noticed, I feel sure, that sentiment is out of fashion. Young people nowadays pride themselves on the stern front they present to any emotional clash, and would rather die than be thought what they call soft and impressionable. You must forgive them on account of the shocking physical dangers two generations of them successively endured. You, although your life on earth witnessed at least forty years of armed conflict, were spared the actual risks of warfare, which occurred overseas. This h. hardened, in the twentieth century—if you like, bruta 's '—not only thought, but fashions in means of express: However, I understand you. I think that the phrase "I ve at first sight" is a very becoming description of the way that, as one of our poets has phrased it, "The pollen blows"!'

Later I thought that this quotation was ill advised. My great-uncle seemed to wince. I hurriedly told myself that biology would hardly be a study in which he was likely to feel any interest, even if he knew of its existence. I seemed to hear him mutter:

'Well, there it is. You see, it happened to me!'

I think this was the most striking pronouncement in the whole of his inexplicable but veritable intercourse with me as his descendant.

The old worn phrase took on a new impressiveness. What did changes in mode of description of any sudden catastrophic event matter? There was the ultimate, the arresting fact. What he recounted had actually happened to him. The results were so indelible that they marked his whole later life and were perpetuated on his tombstone.

He had fallen silent, and I respected his silence. In fact, I dreaded that the lovely calamity of which I knew he was the victim might render him unwilling or incapable of continuing his interchange with me. I shut my eyes, and was even more careful to shut my mouth, or whatever other organ it was that traversed age and condition between us. Slowly I began to feel his evidently urgent desire to make some articulate record of what had happened become alive, like a gradually strengthening broadcast transmission, a 'set, warming up'.

'It was only for an instant, Nephew. Perhaps love at first sight can hardly occur otherwise!'

'I think I know what you mean, Uncle. I have heard a critic speak of the mingling of entranced gaze on the faces of Bacchus and Ariadne, in the picture by Titian in our National Gallery as the "embrace of the glances".' No sooner had the words left my mouth, than I regretted them. My ancestor fell silent, as if he doubted the propriety of his being compared to a heathen deity. If he knew the picture in his later days he might have felt those half-clad figures inappropriate to his way of life and his position in society. But I need not have been apprehensive. He was not thinking of himself, but of the beautiful girl whose first appearance created a vision of such impact on his feelings. I thought I heard him murmur:

'Ariadne' and again, 'Ariadne', as though he accepted a certain resemblance between that figure of the classics, and her whose fate had a fatal attraction, for him, never to be satisfied in life. In order to induce him to tell me more of his feelings at that supreme moment, I added:

'Unless the miniaturist who has left us that striking record of Sophia Goddard has lied, she must have been a young woman of superlative charm.'

He fell silent a moment. These, the only words I could think of at that instant, were, of course, bathos. Quite inadequate. But he was so won by the chance of making plain that meeting, which is only cursorily mentioned in a paragraph of the biography of him as a Norwich worthy, and inferred from the little known of his beloved, that he made no expostulation. He seemed to welcome them. Again he gave such a sigh that one almost expected the surface of the portrait to rise and fall.

'Words are useless,' I thought I heard him declare. 'Even the miniature gives little idea of what you so rightly call her charm. For during that fleeting moment I had no opportunity to examine that strong profile, so pure in outline. The curls you see clustered were confined by one of those bonnets of that day, tied below the chin with a riband, arching over the forehead, and concealing the ears. From the throat fell a garment I have an idea was known as a pelisse. That apparel, I, as a male spectator of feminine fashion, have not sufficient knowledge to criticise or even describe. With all that, or without it, nothing could dim the piercing authority of that soul-wounding flash of the eye, at once recognising in me some quality for which she yearned, and startled by the instantaneous and permanent awareness of our mutual response. Had we been free to converse, I feel that I know as well as if I had heard her declaim the words in one of the great speeches I was to hear her deliver in the rôles that were to be speedily allotted to her:

' "This is for ever!" she would have said. And as the words would have rung round the auditorium, I, had I been a member of the audience, might have been tempted to rise in my place and echo:

' "This is for ever" in answer.'

He paused a moment, recovered himself from the emotion the recital had caused him, and as I shut my eyes, from a feeling of intrusion into something at once so sacred and so private, I heard his tone drop to the more habitual level, of what must have been his thoughts for thirty years of his life, and the ensuing period as a portrait.

'That is all there is to say. That is what occurred. It recurs again and again, whenever your companions in this room of yours gaze upon the portrait of me and ask questions, or refer to the various accounts of my life, so full, pleasant and ordinary, hers so brilliant and so brief. Most of all, when you, who are of my blood, the grandchild of my niece who was named after her, at my demand, are present. Your inquiries and thoughts about me, hanging here, made me able to indulge in that exercise of which I am never tired, the telling to anyone who will listen, as you do, with the ear of the spirit, to the story of how Almighty Providence, as Dr. Enfield taught me to believe, created one of his fairest creatures. And then, as if her qualities that were fairer still, were too good for mortal commerce, withdrew her from the light of day, from audiences who applauded, from friends who loved, from me who adored.'

I could not but share the deep feeling he put into these ordinary words, as if he were trying to make circumstantial the tragedy in which he had been involved. I had a feeling that if I did not break in upon his recital, he might continue, and give me more of it, and, after a pause, he did:

'No sooner had that supreme signal flashed between us, than her companion moved her imposing and authoritative figure between us, and swept her away down the long series of dressing-room doors that lined the passage. The two figures disappeared. I stood as if fixed to the floor. I felt one or two of the denizens of that place push past me. For a moment I was seized by a violent trembling of the limbs. But I took command over myself, turned aside to avoid the traffic in the narrow, encumbered passage and sought the door to the street.'

He paused again, and I felt for him and with him so acutely, that I ventured to show my sympathy with his predicament at that supreme moment:

'You must have had great powers of self control,' I ventured, 'not to run after them.'

'No,' he rejoined, 'I avoided that, or anything that might have caused her the least discomposure or offended the chaperone who was with her. It was not only that. The encounter of her eyes with mine was to me somehow so utterly personal and private, that I could not bear to show what I had felt, and still less to allow anyone to guess that I knew . . . I *knew* . . .' (my great-uncle's voice would have risen had he been speaking to me) 'that she had felt an equal, answering, and mortal pang.'

I tried to look as if I understood, not what he had felt, of course, that was confined between him and his soul's-mate, but at least as if I were attentive to the effort he made to convey the story to me. Anyhow, he continued:

'I had gone no farther than the door, when I remembered that Pooley had obtained an entrance for me, and I pushed my way back past the doorkeeper, who was fortunately at that moment engaged in an altercation with some other person. I knew my way down the little steps, to the narrow wicket that opened under the tier of boxes, and gave access to the Pit.

'They were playing *The Merchant of Venice* and I scanned with trembling fingers the list of the cast, many of the names of which had become familiar. There were some new ones, but none that could identify. But as the play proceeded I had a mounting feeling of excitement. Somehow, in spite of several famous names, and many of sufficient if secondary repute, I found myself singling out the actress who took the part of Nerissa. The name standing opposite this part, meant little or nothing to me. I had seen it before, on many a varied list. But somehow, it was the simplicity, the poetic exaltation lent to this by no means prominent part, that bore in upon me that the player portraying the character must be she with whom I had had this brief, crucial encounter. However, I made no further attempt to verify what after all, in my state of excited anticipation might well be a complete delusion. Nor, if my instincts were correct, would she welcome any intrusion on her privacy, and would her guardian or relative permit it? With iron firmness I forced my way through the crowds that poured homewards when the curtain descended and the applause had ceased. I challenged the keen looks of the good people who kept my lodging. The husband noticed the lateness of the hour and remarked upon it:

' "I hope at least you have employed the time profitably?"

'I felt I could not abuse the decent interest in my welfare and answered frankly enough:

' "I witnessed the play at Drury Lane Theatre."

'This confession led the good people to shake their heads,

and to warn me to be on my guard. For although the play might be one of the most famous in the language, the associations of the theatre were such as to need constant watchfulness to avoid the most deplorable results:

' "Many a young man has been attracted by this play-acting. Remember that it is but a parade of assumed appearances, speaking a language not of ordinary commerce, that, whatever its reputation with people of education, can always be read and appreciated without frequenting a place which has the most shocking connections?'

'I assured them that I would give the fullest weight to their kindly meant observations, and begged them to witness that I had come home, with all reasonable speed, and in a state of perfect sobriety, which they could always testify, if inquiry, as I sometimes suspected, might be made by my employers, or even by my parents in Norwich.

'And then, will you credit me, Nephew, I sought my plain if comfortable bedroom and made ready for the night. Such was my exhaustion from so much emotional excitement, that I slept long and dreamlessly, and awoke refreshed.

'Ah! But that morning. Never again could I be the same John Harrison Yallop as before. I traversed the hurrying crowds of the London streets, with a beating heart and eager footsteps. I could not confess what was stimulating the most ordinary actions, in arriving at my place of business. I have a dim memory that more than one woman, against whom I stumbled, smiled at me. And when I glanced in a near-by shop window to discover why this should be, found that I was smiling myself. When I reached the shop, Pooley was not in a mood similar to mine:

' "What makes you so spry?" he demanded, with a touch of humour!

' "It's a lovely morning. I am interested to know what transactions we shall be asked to carry out."

' "Is that all! Let me tell you that it is a very ordinary morning, rather overcast. We shall have the usual attempts to induce us to sell the firm's wares for less than they are worth, and the partners will not be pleased."

' "Perhaps we shall be sent out to make inquiries or convey repaired goods or bespoken purchases."

'Pooley went on half-heartedly to displace the shutters, and carry them down to the cellar in which they were stored. I sternly repressed the questions that were forming on my lips.

' "I'm tired of it all. I'm not sure . . ."

'He did not continue with any threat to change his employment, or even to spend his evenings in a more enjoyable manner. I endeavoured to cheer him for he was normally a good enough fellow.

' "Let's go to one of the gardens, or Astleys," I suggested. "Or shall we see what there is at the Lane?"

'I hoped to bring him round to the subject that was so urgently of interest to me.

'But he remained ill-humoured: "I don't know that I care," was all he would reply.

' "Didn't you have a good evening's entertainment?" I asked. "I thought the play of *The Merchant of Venice* was a delightful spectacle. Do you happen to know who was playing the part of Nerissa?"

' "Yes, I know who should have played it." There was deceptiveness about Pooley. If you led him on a little, you soon discovered his inmost thoughts.

' "Selina should have been put up as the understudy, or so she says!"

'This was what had put him out of humour! That cal-

lous and self-interested girl, I guessed, had kept him dangling about, with assertions which she may have liked to
think true, and had been disappointed, and I daresay
invoked her ill-humour on my unfortunate companion.

' "Who, then, stood in, by preference?"

' "There's a new person, come up from Margate."

' "Margate!" I had never been to the town, and only knew
it by casual references in conversation. "What was her
name," I ventured with dry lips and a choking throat. I
failed to master my feelings as I would have preferred, and
Pooley gave me a sharp look:

' "That's the new *ingénue*," he told me. "She thinks herself no comman clay, I can tell you. The other members of
the company find her unconscionably superior. So if you
are struck with admiration, you can save yourself the trouble
of trying to obtain an introduction!" And he shook his head
and made various gestures at the very thought which he
probably considered as comic and entertaining. Thus, at
the cost of the most bitter disappointment, I had succeeded
in alleviating Pooley's malaise, increasing my own.

' "Her name is Goddard, if that is any pleasure to you,"
he continued. "Sophia Goddard. She takes herself with a
seriousness that has caused a good deal of amusement!'

'I did not know how to receive this. Was it just reflection
of Pooley's own discomfort at the baiting and trailing-about
to which Selina treated him? Was he himself interested in
that beautiful creature, whose brief encounter had occasioned us both, so poignant, and, so I liked to believe,
mutual a thrill?" Pooley did not spare me.

' "And I will tell you further, Miss Goddard is in the
care of a real old she-dragon, who goes everywhere with
her. A party called Plumstead!"

' "A relative?" I managed to stammer out.

' "No one seems to know, but she has complete control of Miss Goddard, and never leaves her . . ."

'It was my turn to be disconcerted and I can assure you, Nephew, I recall now the effort I made to master my feelings, to interest myself in the morning's business, and never to let something near despair appear in my address to Pooley, our employers and the customers. It was a different matter when I turned my steps towards my lodging in the evening. I dreaded being left alone, with the forbidding prospect held out to me by Pooley. I had moments of a fierce desire, to thrust past the doorkeeper, at the Lane, to proffer some sort of appeal, almost demand to Mrs. Plumstead, to make my way by any and every means into the presence of one whom I even then regarded as my heavensent, and chosen destiny.

'How little we know, Nephew, of the intricate and inscrutable methods of Providence! My initial state of uncertainty was not fated to be prolonged. For many days (it cannot have really been long but it then seemed an eternity) I avoided Pooley and did not accompany him to the Theatre. I shut myself up in a room, or on fine evenings took my book to one of the public parks. I read over and over again the lines allotted to Nerissa, with tears in my eyes! Then, with the utmost irrelevance and by the remotest of chances, a couple of fashionably dressed young men appeared in the shop and began making inquiries for necklaces, bracelets and trinkets. My employer made the usual cautionary signs to me, and I hovered near the door, in case of any attempt at dishonest trickery. But these two were open and candid enough:

' "What say you to this?" one demanded of the other, holding up a necklace of medium value but finished with brilliant workmanship.

' "That might work the oracle! Let's see what old Midas says!"

'This seemed to be their playful way of alluding to our very honest and well disposed employer. He gave them some particulars of the finish and the price:

' "You old reprobate!" continued the joker, "don't you ever reflect that you can't take your ill-gotten gains with you? Take my advice, and begin lightening your burden for the journey!"

' "You're all at odds, Charles," interrupted his friend. "Let's use his long experience and knowledge. You, sir," he took my employer by the button of his coat, "have a vast experience of the taste and whims of young ladies. Now, what would you suggest from your stock, that might induce a very highborn and fanciful one to look kindly on the friendship of my young friend here? What are you asked for, sirrah! most often, and what sort of all these gawds do you find most readily acceptable to the fairest and most difficult of their sex, who throng your shop, we feel sure, when they are in funds?"

'He burst out laughing as much at my employer's face as his own wit. A lot more of this badinage continued, but at the end of their visit, the gentlemen left an order, and my employer confided a parcel to my hands.

' "Take this to Drury Lane Theatre, as soon as the artistes begin to assemble, and deliver it to this lady!"

'I hardly knew how to conceal my feelings, when I saw that the package was addressed "Miss Sophia Goddard". Perhaps something of what I was feeling showed in my face and manner in spite of my efforts to appear diligent in the commission confided to me; for he added:

' "You know your way, don't you? If not, Pooley will be able to help you. He has run several of these errands for us."

'Of course I consulted Pooley, who seemed rather amused:

' "Why, that's the very thing for you. Try and look as if you had brought the goods on your own behalf, and not for these young Bucks!"'

'He made great game of my good fortune and gave much superfluous advice as to how to treat the doorkeeper and so forth. But he himself was not going in the same direction, and hinted that he had a more gratifying appointment. He let it be understood that he was being allowed to entertain his Selina, and I did not press him. In the evening, I must admit that I took more than ordinary care with my appearance, and set out for the Lane all too early. As a result, of course, I had to spend some time, my package under my arm, patrolling the neighbouring alleys. At length I saw the usual drawing near of conveyances and foot passengers, singly or in groups, as those who were due to play that night began gathering to make themselves ready. I was agreeably surprised to find the old doorkeeper must have been well liquored up by friends or acquaintances, for he greeted me with far better humour than he had often showed when I had had to depend on Pooley's longer acquaintance, and earlier ground-baiting of him. He was even jocular:

' "Well, young feller, and what have you got in that parcel? Something better than Christmas pudden?" He liked to affect the country speech he assumed must be familiar to me, from my being of provincial origin.

'I told him what was my errand and he sped me forward with encouragement:

' "There's nothing like tryin'," he asserted. "You never know your luck. It's number seventeen!"'

'I found my way through the usual backstage bustling of

those who were late, and loiterings of others who were hope-
ful, and knocked at the door named with a beating heart.

'It was opened and I was admitted to the little lobby by
the dresser, and could hear voices beyond. Then, in
masterful tone: "Come in, whoever you are. What do you
want?"

'Admitted into the dressing-room, I was faced by the
person of the full-figured and unwelcoming Mrs. Plumstead, who took my parcel from my hand and listened to
the usual message with which such were delivered, undid
and examined it.

' "Here, my dear." She passed on the description of the
contents. "It's from that young Carnaby. Do you want to
see what he's sent, or shall I pack it off? It's pretty enough,
but you know what he means."

'This short pause while she opened it, and read the card
enclosed, allowed me to give a peep beyond her. And there,
reflected in the mirror while the dresser was sorting out
her costume, my glance sought and met that of the being
who in all the world held the shape of my fate in her hands,
as if the precious fingers were closed on my heart.'

My uncle's voice seemed to rise and deepen at the memory. The words seemed to be forced from him:

'There, in her beloved return of my eager look, I saw
glad surprise, recognition, even a faint amusement that in
such a place, at such a time, we should enjoy the fleeting
communion that cannot have lasted seconds, but which
seemed like the threshold of eternity. While that sacred
interchange lasted, I heard her voice, as of some other person in a different world were making use of some other
language:

' "It's very obliging of Mr. Carnaby. Of course I don't
accept such a present!"

'The few words were delivered as if they were in some spoken part, alien a whole universe from the momentary engagement of our eyes with each other. I heard the much louder, firm and decisive accents of Mrs. Plumstead, as she refolded the container she had undone, and passed it back to me:

' "There, young man, take the goods back to your employer, and let him acquaint the sender that they have been politely and firmly refused!"

'I had just sense enough to tear my eyes from that faintly smiling image that, even through the half-completed make-up visible in the mirror, demanded all the firmness I could muster to force my limbs to withdraw into the common tarnished everyday, of life behind the scenes. With a thumping pulse and feet unsteady with the violence of my feelings, I left the stage door and returned to my lodging. Making excuses to my landlady, I devoured my supper and went to my room. Securing my parcel for return to the shop in the morning, I sank into a delicious reminiscent mood, until sleep prevailed.'

4

What can Nature do?

DURING some weeks of lovely autumn weather, I had leisure, from time to time, to indulge in these queer ... what shall I call them? ... interviews ... I felt them to be. The word 'séances' is used for an utterly different type of communication. These moments of what I felt to be almost living conversation with my uncle were not governed by theory or arranged by any plan. They arose, as I have shown, from a chance remark of a fellow townsman, with whom I was not very intimate. I did not feel I was being made by any outside force to discover any more than I had ever known before, of my relative's decent but unremarkable life, in which there was embedded the startling brief tragic love story, like a jewel accidentally framed in an unexpected and unlikely setting. If I had been asked ... and the very supposition shows how remote was the chance ... I should have answered, quite sincerely, that it just happened so. I fell easily into the mood which my ancestor enjoyed, he would have said, through the teaching of Dr. Enfield. I can almost hear him: 'Divine Providence has a sacred purpose. We may perceive it. We cannot pretend to understand its motive!' He might even add:

'You yourself, Nephew, have already asked, with no hope of logical answer, what made so many bullets miss you and left you a survivor amid so many less fortunate!'

G

That great imponderable seemed to dominate my interchange with my great-uncle. After days that passed like so many others, these many years, with his portrait hanging on the wall, I passing before it, or not, if I did not happen to enter that room, on that particular day. But even if I did, nothing happened. I was otherwise engaged, and he just hung there, handsome, mellow, inviting no greetings, getting none. And then, for no reason I can discover, some chance led me to seat myself in my chair, with no pressing call on my time. My glance would fall on his sub-fusc gleaming surface, and somehow he would wish me, or was it I that wished? . . . to know more of his passion for Sophia Goddard. I have even wondered if the old armchair, one of a set of his period I happen to have inherited, exerted some influence, when I was seated in it. But I am no believer in such semi-occult connections, and found it sometimes possible to direct my thoughts to him and to feel him, if I am right, wishing to direct his to me, when I was not in that chair, or any of the set. So I place no importance on that contact. Just like that, I chanced to be sitting and I suppose I followed up some recollection of what I had last had of his story, and of hers, the fatal dedicated girl, and I framed the question:

'The time came when your engagement to Mr. Vineyard Perkins terminated. You returned home. And by what any unbelieving person would probably call sheer coincidence, Sophia Goddard happened to join the stock company at the Theatre Royal, that Thomas Ivory had built in Norwich, near the Assembly Rooms?

'It can't be as improbable as that, Uncle. To me the word coincidence is useless. It simply means that two things happen to meet. Utterly inhuman, isn't it?' And he seemed to agree:

'Just so, Nephew. There again Almighty Providence had a purpose. It brought me to the back passages, behind the scenes at Drury Lane, on some errand I have forgotten, it was so disconnected with its decisive result.'

'I suppose you were often enough sent to deliver parcels? Or did you seek the chance to elude old Northgate, the doorkeeper, and slip into the auditorium, in the hope, or was it with the knowledge ... that Sophia would be appearing in a minor part or understudying a better one?'

'It all grows misty, not so much with the lapse of years, as with the diminishing importance of such detail. The next in the train of events stamped on my memory, runs in that worn, encumbered shapeless world of Back Stage, trodden by many a hurrying or dawdling figure, dominated by great grotesque pieces of scenery, "sets", cardboard mountains and make-believe woods, one-dimension palaces and temples. The whole merges into a dim background, and against it stands out a familiar figure, and a less known one, that had been named to me, and which I regarded with awe.'

'What familiar figure, in that strange world?'

'Not strange to him, Nephew. It was that of Mr. John Brunton, from Theatre Royal, Norwich. He was familiar with it all.'

'Ah, and he recognised you?'

'Only just. He knew my face, from having seen me with my parents, who had a certain modest standing in Norwich. I stood rooted to the spot, and he gave a second look, and a nod, as if to say he vaguely recognised me but what was I doing there?'

'He didn't greet you?'

'No. He was deep in conversation with his companion, whom I recognised as Mrs. Plumstead and the other Mr. Wroughton, the manager. They passed me by. I heard some discussion as to the merits and availability of an *ingénue*, which Mr. Brunton was seeking for his stock company.

'The next link in the twisted chain of events, with which I was entangled, came through no stranger source than that of my good father's weekly letter. Amid a homely report of local happenings, which he naturally felt important, because it was Norwich life, and expected me to feel important because I was Norwich bred, occurred the words, in his plain, careful script:

' " . . . *I went with your mother to secure places for the play he is giving, last evening. There I came upon Mr. John Brunton, who mentioned that he had seen you, engaged on some commission on behalf of your employers at Drury Lane Theatre. He hoped very civilly that you were prospering in your training in London, which I made known to him. I replied that you seemed to be making good progress, and that I hoped Mr. Dunham would soon find you sufficiently experienced, to allow of his according you a partnership in Norwich. For I must say, my dear boy, that your mother and I do not grow any younger. I fear she is failing, and when I ask Dr. Lubbock, he smiles kindly enough, and says we can none of us live for ever. True enough, I felt bound to reply to him, but it was his business to see that we did not go before our time through neglect. This brought from him the pleasant assurance that he knows she is well looked after in my house. The feeling remains that, if you are content, I might ask Mr. Dunham for the terms on which he would admit you to partnership and these I will acquaint you of, hoping . . . indeed trusting that you are still conscious of the bonds of family affection."* '

I could not help feeling that it was unlikely that my great-uncle had retained the verbiage of his father's letter so completely, but the passage of intelligence between us was already so unusual a matter, that I just accepted the sense of what was conveyed and listened eagerly for the results of what he had told me so far.

'So, not without regrets, I took my leave of Mr. Vineyard Perkins, in his shop in Dorset Square. He very civilly offered me a glass of madeira, and wished me every success in the profession he felt I was well qualified to enter. He asked for some particulars of Mr. Dunham's business, and nodded approval of what I was able to tell him. He even undertook to put in the way of Mr. Dunham and myself any small items of business that came to his knowledge, as being required in Norwich.'

My great-uncle gave a slight cough of satisfaction at the memory, as if a lingering after taste of the Perkins madeira was agreeable to his throat.

'My parting with the good people with whom I had lodged with so much convenience, and kind-hearted provision for my welfare, also left nothing but the most pleasant recollections. Brick Lane was not a district where one's fancy recalls scenes that one hesitates to discard from one's memory. Yet the rooms had always been clean and well kept, and the landlord and landlady were touchingly concerned for my future. They gave me as a parting gift, a volume of sermons, which I promised to peruse, if in my inmost thoughts I reflected that I should submit them first to Dr. Enfield for approval.'

'So you left with no deep regrets, and the pleasant anticipation of advancement in your native town?'

'Never more lively than when I felt the coach topping the last rise, by the Town Close Estate, and saw before me the ancient walls of Norwich, the City Gates through which

Queen Elizabeth and his Majesty King Charles the Second had passed, all those years before me. Above the battlements of the walls, I saw the outline of the grim old castle that had outfaced so many centuries, and so much diverse fortune, and there, behind it, as if to show that the heaven-aspiring thoughts of all the worshippers of all those years, arose from the firm loyalties of the Norman Keep, there soared to the sky, the delicate tapering shape of the spire of the Cathedral. I was home. In a very few moments I traversed the market place, and sought the door of my parents' house in the Gentleman's Walk.'

He paused a moment and I took the opportunity to intervene to complete my knowledge of my great-uncle's stay in London:

'You had much to tell your parents that you had never fully explained in your letters home. Did you give any account of your fellow assistant Pooley?'

'That, and all such matter, you may be sure were the object of their questions. I could give no very happy account of Pooley. He had been very indifferently treated by his Selina as the days went by. She and her fellows of the less-distinguished ranks of the Drury Lane Company, had none of the devotion that I felt for Sophia Goddard, and she for me. Pooley admitted that they were only too glad that she had been chosen by Mr. John Brunton, to transfer to the stock company at Norwich. In his less harassed mood, Pooley admitted that Selina and the others had asked him with derision if the great Miss Goddard was going to play to the "Turnip tops" as they characterised the Norwich audience, having little idea that the titled and landed occupants of the stalls at Drury Lane, might just as easily be found, when staying on their estates in the country, in the boxes of the Theatre Royal Norwich where my parents were ready enough to point out to me, Lord Orford, or some member of the Wyndham or Astley families.'

'So you took your leave of Pooley, who stayed on as assistant to Mr. Vineyard Perkins?'

'Such was his intention when I left. I did ask him if he would like his name mentioned to Mr. Dunham as soon as my agreement on the partnership should be completed. But at this he withdrew somewhat; he said he still hoped to form a permanent attachment with Selina, and that in any case, he would not be prepared to suggest to her that she "buried herself in the country" as he put it, I think at her suggestion.'

'So you parted. Did you ever know what he did with himself, later?'

'I do not think his was a very happy story. I was able to be of some trifling support to him from time to time. But I think eventually he wore himself out in the irregular and disappointing mode of life that he was drawn into!'

'I'm sure you were kindness itself, Uncle. That is how you have always appeared in your portrait and I know how enlightened were your principles. I am sure your private generosity was no less. And you owed Pooley some indirect and accidental advantages. It was he who made you familiar with the stage door of Drury Lane. He contributed, if little and unintentionally, to what was to be the dominating passion of your life!'

'Such is the involved unpredictable pattern of life, Nephew. The strands of our being cross and entwine, then separate and fall apart. You must have experienced similar encounters yourself!'

'Oh, mine has been simple and happy, calm and straightforward, once I survived the carnage that ravaged my generation. But you felt the impact of a fatal attraction, the sombre gravity of which I never knew.'

My great-uncle paused, and I could almost feel him taking control of his emotions, as he prepared to hand on to me some impression of the crisis towards which he was slowly but inevitably moving in his communication with me. I was careful not to let my eagerness to learn of it jar or embarrass him. A certain delicacy about the portrait forbade me.

'I asked my father, if he or any of his acquaintances had remarked any special personalities among the recruitment with which Mr. John Brunton had been strengthening his company at the Theatre Royal. But my dear old father was not so familiar with the dramatic items, or interested in the portrayal of character, to have singled out the one possible name on which all my thoughts were precariously centred. At length I brought myself to scan the playbills of the week following my return home.

'There it was, the name that might, in my vision, have been written in letters of fire.

' "Miss Sophia Goddard." There followed the list of some of the rôles in which she was to appear. My hands trembled. I spilled my tea and suffered the natural reproaches my mother made in her now rather feeble and halting voice, as she summoned the maid to put straight the disorder I had occasioned.'

The little domestic scene, in the old house over the glover's shop on the Gentleman's Walk was plain enough to me, and I had no difficulty in hearing the half-jocular clucking: 'The boy's rather excited. He's going to see Staff the lawyer and Mr. Dunham will go through the deed of partnership with him,' and the reproof, 'Let's hope he won't spill the ink when he signs!'

My great-uncle took up the thread of that long ago morning:

'Little did my good parents guess the real reason of my

WHAT CAN NATURE DO? 101

agitation. The morning interview, which made me a partner in the goldsmiths', silversmiths' and jewellers' business
at the corner of Davey Place, is now all forgotten and vanished in the sands of time. The affectionate approval of my
parents, their contentment at seeing me started upon the
road, they felt sure, of success, I hope I duly appreciated
and looked grateful. In fact I was burning to cross the market, penetrate White Hart Yard; for better concealment, I
was so sensitive as to the errand on which I was bound. The
doorkeeper at the Theatre Royal, in Chapel Field Lane,
was a provincial version of stern old Northgate with whom
I had become so familiar during my visits to Drury Lane.
Moreover, he knew me slightly, from knowing my parents,
and replied to my inquiry, which I strove to make with no
sign of the urgency of my feelings, but as if it were some
matter of business.

'Old Fiddament, as his name was, answered: "Miss Goddard. She lodges with Mrs. Curtis, in St. Gregory's, same as
Mrs. Siddons did. You'll have to state your business. They
don't have no gallivanting there!"'

'I might have drawn some comfort from that statement
made in the doorkeeper's nonchalant plainness. The officers
of the garrison had no doubt pressed Fiddament for just
that information and had probably tipped him for it. I made
the best I could of the time that must elapse before I could
profit by it. Sophia was billed that night to take the place of
Miss Esmead as Elvira!'

'It must have been a great occasion for you, Uncle, to see
her on your local stage and know that you would be able to
seek her company after the performance.'

'My dear boy, I could hardly keep my seat. If she had
shone with brilliance, among the leaders of the profession
at Drury Lane, you may guess how she appeared among

Mr. Brunton's solid and hard-working stock company, reinforced as it was, by the recruits such as she, he had obtained
from London.'

'I am sure you behaved with the utmost discretion.'

My uncle sighed. 'Discretion is said to be the better part
of valour. I knew it only as a means of stifling the hammer-
ing of my heart against my ribs.'

'And when the curtain descended?'

'I slunk hesitantly to the stage door. As I had anticipated,
among the loungers and sightseers there were many who
for mere admiration, curiosity or vanity, knew or claimed to
know, the members of the company as they emerged, some
hurrying to avoid unwelcome attention, others by no means
unwilling to run the gauntlet of exclamation, greeting or
invitation. At length two well-shrouded figures passed
through the vociferous little crowd, acknowledging no ac-
costing and hurrying along in the shadow of the wall of the
Assembly House, and crossing into Lady's Lane. From
their manner, the ample stature of the one, the silent and
rapt reserve of the other, I had no difficulty in recognising
Mrs. Plumstead and Sophia.

'I followed them, across Bethel Street and Lower Goat
Lane by the Quaker Meeting, but by the time they had
reached St. Gregory's, they had thrown off all notice and
pursuit, and I was alone, upon their tracks. This led me to
consider what welcome I could expect, if I attempted to
introduce myself when they reached Mrs. Curtis's lodging.
I slackened my paces, so that they would not hear my
steps and assume they were being followed. They reached
Mrs. Curtis's door and disappeared. I turned moodily
home, and spent a night of discomfort and uncertainty. Can
you see the difference, Nephew, between the sudden joyful
recognition of each other in the unaccustomed atmosphere,

an hurried instant of back stage that seemed to insulate us from all the world, and the comparatively difficult and confusing problem of how to renew and confirm that supreme moment, in the well-known surroundings of my native place, which had become the scene unexpectedly of her repose and leisure?'

'Yes, I think I can, Uncle. You had to provide for the inevitable challenges and inquiries you were bound to meet, once it became evident to any third party, especially one in the position of Mrs. Plumstead, that a chance encounter was to be renewed and repeated!'

'I am glad of your understanding and sympathy. I did what still seemed natural to me, brought up as I had been. I screened my perturbed feelings, and looks haggard from want of sleep, behind the anxieties natural to a young man, assessing for the first time, the responsibilities he was assuming, on taking up a partnerhip, in a firm of some standing, and length of reputation. Apparently I was successful. No remarks were made other than those Mr. Dunham very naturally addressed to me, as he showed me the stock for which I was to be partially responsible, his methods of business, for cash or account, and his lists of old and frequent customers, and the less dependable public that came and went with the day to day traffic of the Gentleman's Walk, and the one or two exceptional items, such as cleaning and repairing of the Civic Regalia, which were entrusted to his hands.'

'That must have been interesting. I know how good and extensive is the valuable collection of objects of the finer metals, which an ancient corporation like that of Norwich has amassed. Some speak of it as rivalling the King John Sword and Cup, at King's Lynn, and even draw comparison with that at the Guildhall in London.'

My uncle seemed to swell slightly with pride in the trust imposed on the firm he had joined, but it can only have been the changing light, as the autumn day varied the reflected sunshine that indirectly reached the portrait. But I wanted him to be spared the sensation that I was probing through mere curiosity, the emotions that had once wrung his heart. I tried to soften the impact of violent longing, the faith-demanding gap that separated him from closer intimacy with that feminine spirit he felt to be twinned with his own.

'It has always rather amused me to notice that except for the Sword of Honour, the two great gilt maces presented by the Howard and Walpole families, and the most precious of all, the mace of rock crystal and the silver mace heads, nearly all the possessions of the Corporation, are for the purpose of eating and drinking!'

My great-uncle may not have noticed the diversion I had attempted, to spare him too continued pressure of nostalgic memory, and exalted selflessness which might be more than any image of paint and canvas could sustain. From moment to moment I sometimes feared that our tenuous contact might be brought to an end by sheer impossibility of such fine devotion being transmitted. I was relieved to find that he felt that the civic plate was after all a very natural shape for such uses as City Fathers required of it.

'You see,' he seemed to explain, 'there was always the St. George's Feast, every year. And many a celebration in those days, of triumphs in the warfare in which we were continuously engaged, or of some local matter of importance, such as Property Tax. There was the meeting at which the Norwich and Norfolk Savings Bank was inaugurated.'

Here he seemed to hesitate and I knew why. One of the great days of the use of Norwich Corporation plate was that on which he was welcomed home from his journey to present the Address in favour of Reform, which gained him his knighthood from a sympathetic Sovereign. I did not interrupt him, and with a sigh, as I thought, he resumed.

'No, when I had disposed of what were to me the lesser affairs of the day, I sought Dr. Enfield. My beloved pastor had for long been in indifferent health. In fact I, and a few who knew his beneficence and loved his character, felt that so lofty a spirit was subject to more than the average wear and tear, in the daily life of the City as it was in those days. For no amount of civic banqueting could disguise the desperate poverty and helpless unhandiness of so large a portion of the population in the yards and courts where they existed, one could hardly say lived!'

'That, of course, was what prompted you to present the case for Reform, which became one of the major purposes of your later life.'

'To me, and to those who agreed with me, there was no possibility of improving the general level of the living standards of so many of our fellow citizens, until the representation of political opinion was placed on a more honest basis.'

My great-uncle's voice seemed to fade and his presence in his portrait to recede, as we knitted our thoughts together on those long-ago social and political projects. He became ... what shall I call it ...? more sentient when we turned to the vital passion that lent so much deeper a tone to our intercourse.

'You felt you must consult Dr. Enfield about your desperate need to approach Sophia?'

'I do not know, Nephew, what has moved you in your life, as that attachment moved me, or to whom you could turn, certain of convincing and enlightening advice, such as

I felt sure I should receive from him. I told him of our instantaneous recognition of each other, like nothing else in my life save Titian's representation of the meeting of Bacchus and Ariadne. He heard me with that close, deeply sympathetic attention I expected and received. I recall the substance of part at least of the reply he made, all the more impressive, on account of the demand it made on his slowly lessening powers, which he met, as he always did in his short but full life, at the pleading of those whom he felt, as he did in my case, to have a call upon him.'

'From Dr. Enfield's portrait I should expect just that!'

'You will not be disappointed with what I can recall of that long ago exchange in the old parsonage house in Colegate. It comes back to me like this':

My great-uncle's personality seemed to acquire a deeper, more impressive character.

' "My dear boy, the attraction you felt so suddenly and so overwhelmingly, is not necessarily passing and momentary on that account. It may well be that you have now encountered, from what you tell me, an influence that may well establish itself in your life, and only cease, as we believe all mortal contacts do, with death." '

My great-uncle's voice rose and became stirring in gravity. ' "If then" ' (he added, and I knew he was thinking that Dr. Enfield's reservation had in fact been borne out by the death-outlasting devotion to his Sophia). He went on:

' "It appears that this is one of the crucial tests that Almighty Providence presents before us. We cannot tell, when we give and take vows, with some other person, if we have the courage and steadfastness to maintain them. I happen to be one of those to whom it has been easy and comfortable. You have probably guessed, from such observation as you have been able to make of Mrs. Enfield . . ." his face was illumined by a tender reminiscent smile, "that in our case, we just never wanted to be closely, physically united with anyone else. For that is the ultimate test, my dear boy..." '

My great-uncle allowed himself a decorous, affectionate smile. I knew why. When Dr. Enfield used that term, my uncle was already approaching his thirties and had just 'set up in business', as the saying was. But he accepted and indeed welcomed his revered pastor's view of him as a boy...

' "When the momentary flash of illumination that revealed you and your Sophia to one another had left only an impression on your two spirits, as the light of a lamp leaves on the retina when the flame is extinguished, do you feel... and do you feel she feels... that you will be able to support, not merely those exalted moments, but the daily round of contact of your house? Will you be able to accommodate yourselves to the sharing of house and board, and bed, as well as the joys and sorrows, the risks and the triumphs of married life?" '

My uncle's voice took on a tone of strain and I knew why. He had repeated the sense of Dr. Enfield's words, which had envisaged a future for the John and Sophia of those days, that was destined never to be realised. I sat forbidden, trying to enter into the feelings of that long ago tragedy. My uncle went on:

'Of course, I soberly answered Dr. Enfield's searching query. I felt sure that I could never have enough of Sophia. I dared to believe she could never have too much of me. It is now melancholy to reflect that the ultimate proof of the devotion to which Dr. Enfield set so high a standard, was never to be fully demanded. But I gave my word. He replied: "I believe you, John. In that case you are justified in making to her the proposition that you should join your lives together. I hope I may be granted health and strength to preside at the ceremony, if she is willing." '

My uncle seemed to have mastered the depth of feeling, that I could sense, invading his memories. I may have looked as if I thought I knew what he felt. He continued with calm fortitude:

'I can now regard that reinforcing advice with calmness. Death is irretrievable and final. It *has* to be accepted.'

My uncle's voice grew momentarily stern then lifted a little:

'I at least, of all that great proportion of the human race to whom it has happened to be faced by Death of a loved one, have been allowed a respite. I have been permitted to make a record, cut in stone, that will outlast, at least the memory of many generations. Sophia will not be forgotten for the foreseeable future!'

He ceased (or was it that I lost contact, because he receded into his inarticulate self?) Gradually the contact reasserted itself. He 'warmed up' and the communication he was making and which I was so anxious to receive, was re-established. I heard:

'But at least I knew what to do. I hope you may have had someone whose opinion will support and guide you in some crisis of your life, when you most need it.' There was a pause, and then I seemed to see rather than hear him: 'I controlled the agitation of my feelings, Nephew. I even began to try to express them in writing with the idea of sending them to Sophia. But they were too strong for me. I felt the urgent need of a decision, and the following afternoon, at the time I knew from my experiences at Drury Lane she would be resting, I made my way to Mrs. Curtis in St. Gregory's, and boldly knocked at the door. After some short delay, it was opened, but I could tell that it was "on the chain". Through the aperture this permitted, I heard the voice, I had no doubt from its broad local accent, of Mrs. Curtis.

' "Who's that?" she demanded.

'I stated my name and my new position, as the partner with Mr. Dunham.

' "And what might you be wanting, young Mr. Yallop?"

'I took a firm stand on the doorstep and announced: "I wish to speak with Miss Goddard."

' "We shall have to hear about that!"

'Standing there, thus denied, Nephew, I began to wonder if I should have done better to deliver, at least a request for an interview in writing. Before very long, however, I saw and heard the chain released, and I was admitted. The door firmly secured behind me, I was bidden to wait, while Mrs. Curtis retired to a back room and held a half-audible consultation. It was apparently favourable, for she returned and invited me to enter.

' "Young Mr. Yallop!" I was announced.

'The pleasant sitting-room looked out on to one of those restricted but pleasant City gardens so common in Norwich. Beside the fire, amid a litter of feminine detail, books that might be acting parts, clothes that might be costumes in repair, with just that informality that I was to grow to expect about anyone engaged in the stage career, two ladies had risen. The one nearer me, to whom I forced myself to turn, was Mrs. Plumstead. There was no immediate welcome in her look, but half-recognition was soon visible on those composed and determined features. Beside her . . .'

My uncle paused and there was a faint vibration, as if the very materials of the portrait were affected by the pulsation of a heart that had once responded.

'Beside her had risen my beloved, her face irradiated by

H

the certainty she felt. With that perfect command, to which her powers as an actress owed so much, she said in the most matter-of-fact voice:

' "It's Mr. Yallop. You remember, he called on me at the Lane. Be seated, sir!"'

'Mrs. Plumstead permitted herself a rather stiff bow, but there was a softening in her expression though no sign that she remembered. Those two words I later felt were an interpolation to reassure the chaperon (if that was what she was).

' "You may leave us, while I learn what has earned us the pleasure of his visit!"'

'This was delivered with that mixture of command and persuasion and brought the reply:

' "I'll have a word with Mrs. Curtis!"'

'How far this was intended as a caution to me I did not know, but Mrs. Plumstead did leave the room, and we were alone together.

'Nephew, I cannot represent my feelings. I can only relive what were the brief but brilliant moments of our intercourse. No words came, my tongue was silenced, my glance perhaps let fly something of what I was feeling, and was met by a look so melting, with anticipation realised, mixed with a delicious mocking, as if the limitations (such as Mrs. Plumstead personified) of our communion were a delightful background to a passion that must not be given its scope. She proffered her hands, taking mine in that firm but delicate grasp I was to grow familiar with. Standing thus opposite, I was bathed in that thrilling and slightly quizzical survey she seemed to enjoy. Her lips moved. In that low but penetrating accent of which she was mistress, I heard her declare: "I knew you would come!"

'The lovely confidence, as if she were bestowing a precious burden on me, wrung from me the query:

' "How?"

'She shook her head and the ringlets danced about her ears.

' "Do you really require to know?"

'Challenged thus, in the depth of my soul, I continued to mutter:

' "I am bold enough to guess."

' "What?"

' "You knew I knew ... we knew each other's mind." And here she burst out laughing, turning that perfect neck, so the white skin glistened and the depth of the dark eyeball, arrested a moment, was displayed brimming, the white teeth lightly set in the curving lips lent an air of restrained connivance. It was but a flash. The delicious half-amused, half-triumphant excitement was too much. She snatched a flimsy piece of lace from her corsage and broke into a paroxysm of coughing, the trim shoulders bent and heaving until I was constrained to support her. In an instant she had recovered, let me lower her upon the chair next to mine and to complete the contrast of wicked enjoyment with burlesque caution, she flung a defying sidelong look in the direction of the door:

' "No, but seriously. It does happen, does it?"

' "Yes. It has happened to us."

' "Out of all the people in the world!"

' "Many miss it."

' "Are we sure?"

'This smiling query, Nephew, sounds very insipid as I repeat it. Emphasised by a half-questioning, half-smiling glance, it made an almost physical appeal to me. Had she laid her hands upon my forearms, and forced me to my knees the effect could not have been stronger or out of character. I sank upon them crying:

' "I am sure. I will prove it if I may know, to whom I must address a formal request for you."

'Then she did lay her hands on mine that I stretched out to her, and arrested them. She turned her head aside, doubt and a pretty confusion overclouded the brilliance of her expression of a moment before.

' "John, dear . . .'

' "Not Mrs. Plumstead?" Somehow I had never felt that Mrs. Plumstead, who had treated me politely enough, had any ultimate authority over her.

' "John, I don't know!"

'This was stupefying. She released my hands. We drew slightly apart, studying each other's faces. I could not bear it. I insisted!'

It was a fact that, at this stage of his recital my great-uncle's voice seemed to rise, or would have done, had we been engaged in normal converse.

' "Dearest, on what other basis can we meet?"

'There was no answer. I took that to require a fuller explanation.

' "If it is not Mrs. Plumstead, there must be someone to whom I can submit an honest offer of marriage."

'Instead of the shy excitement with which such words would meet, I suppose, uttered to the average young woman, she moved her head softly left and right. It was no hasty negative, but a long-drawn, wistful incapacity to reply.'

As he said the words, the scene, in that long-vanished superior 'theatrical' lodging started up before me. I understood as I never had before, that other unaccountable quality in my great-uncle's portrait, the quality which lent a richness of depth that no mere likeness of a prosperous merchant, solid citizen and scrupulous human being could provide.

'Nephew, a kind of mortal anguish rose in my throat and I fear I blundered almost violently:

' "Sophia, I am not boasting. I have a sufficient standing in this City to offer an establishment that need not be despised!"

'She looked at me, as from a great distance, as perhaps Juliet looked at Romeo, if she had, as I had often thought Sophia portrayed her as having, some far-sighted vision that they would never be united. There was silence for a counted minute. Then, as if feeling she had betrayed good manners, she answered softly:

' "I am sure of it. I am not boasting either. I will tell you what I know, but there is no one whose leave must be asked."

'I struggled as if caught in a net and could only appeal: "There is none to sanction our betrothal?"

'Here she broke into a winning guileful smile, that I was to see her use so often when the parts she play demanded it:

' "John dear," she pronounced softly, averting her gaze:

' "You won't love me less because I have no relations?"

'I forget what assurances I gave. She yielded her right hand. But I made a blunder.

' "Then, if there is no one to whom it must be referred, will you not call on my parents, or allow them to call on you. And my partner whom I have joined in business . . ."

'I hastened on: "And then you will be able to give Mr. Brunton your notice that you are leaving the stage, in order to become my wife!"

'I saw in an instant that I had failed to carry her with me in my thoughtless enthusiasm. She stared at me long, in silence, and there crept into the lovely survey an undertone of sadness. Her lower lip quivered, her eyelids dropped, she buried her face in her hands.

'I started forward, seized her by the wrists, would have offered my shoulder, partly as apology for my rough lack of perception, partly to assure her of my intention to make good my word, to love, know and protect her, even if the phrase was premature. But when I lifted her hands she was still dry-eyed, and it was not weakness of grief I saw, so much as bewilderment. She brought it to an end.

' "What a scene I am making! You will agree that I could hardly be prepared for what so many girls would be only too glad to hear."

'I was about to protest that no other girl was ever to hear a similar declaration from me, but she decisively interrupted: "Dear John, do go and find someone less impossible than I. You have so much to offer and I can never accept. . . ."

' "Do you really wish to dismiss me?" I did my very best, Nephew, to speak in a calm and controlled voice. It was not easy, but I hope my sincerity shone through our inexplicable impasse, for she replied:

' "No, John, I will be as sincere as you. I would rather die than that."

'There was an ominous ring in the words. Years after as I, despairing, repeated to myself every utterance of those beloved lips, I felt she knew that she was foretelling the fate that was to overwhelm us. At the moment I did not give full weight to the sweet gravity with which she spoke.

' "Then I may call and see you sometimes. Will Mrs. Plumstead make difficulties?"

' "Oh, no, she is a great resource to us. Not all those who seek my acquaintance, intend to offer, or even pretend to do so, what you generously put forward. Many are undesirable and cause her annoyance and anxiety."

' "And always will," I managed to blurt out, "until these

persons find you have the protection of a man."

' "Then you shall be my safeguard."

' "Sophia, must I say again, how I would like to be much more."

' "It is very sweet to hear. I think we have tried the good woman's patience enough. Let me send for her and make plain the goodwill you bring."

'Mrs. Plumstead joined us and Sophia made no little effort to provide a comfortable place for her, and on the sofa told her.

' "Mr. Yallop has been making me blush by the praise he has bestowed on some of my renderings."

'Here I again, at the risk of overdoing my importunity, addressed the elder lady:

' "Not only that, ma'am, but I have suggested to Miss Goddard that she puts too much of her reserve of strength into the playing of her parts. Might I offer, as an alternative to her very strenuous rehearsals and acting, that she might accept, in your company, occasional holiday trips in the countryside adjoining the City. Perhaps if the season turns fine, we might penetrate as far as the coast!"

'This seemed to be the right line to take. Mrs. Plumstead was at once flattered and reassured, though I felt certain she had made her own inquiries and was convinced of my respectability. I must say that, on my part it was sheer inspiration, whipped up perhaps by the mysterious negative Sophia opposed to my crowning offer.

'I continued the conversation on such matters and learned something of the plans Mr. Brunton had put forward, for the use of Sophia's services, during the coming season. Her début in Norwich had been very successful. From a minor part in *The Beggar's Opera* she had "graduated" as she put it to the lesser Shakespearian heroines. When I mentioned

Portia, she clasped her hands, drew herself up, and spoke some of those immortal lines.

' "That's all very well, my dear," Mrs. Plumstead chid her. "You've had a quiet morning and the pleasure of Mr. Yallop's company. But you know you won't feel so gay when you've had a week of late nights, difficult parts to sustain, and all the chances and changes of your life on the boards."

'Sophia, of course, affectionately made light of these warnings and I was astonished and a little perturbed by the ambitious future she evidently saw for herself, taking Mrs. Siddons and her peers as her example. She revelled in the stories, common I suppose in all the theatres in which famous figures of the stage have played, of audiences whose members fainted, of applause that disorganised the time schedule, the near riots by spectators disappointed at not achieving admission. I began to see, Nephew, a valuable ally in this Mrs. Plumstead whose authority over Sophia was at once so indefinite but apparently willingly conceded. The lady herself loved to work into the conversation her own reminiscences. I gathered from these, and they left nothing to the imagination, that she might have been a "Queen" in a pantomime or even an "Angel" in the fashionable transformation scene.

'While Sophia would be preoccupied with her chances of playing Ophelia or Desdemona (and there was something slightly ominous to me in her fondness for parts that end in fatality) Mrs. Plumstead would intervene with her own recollections, and I am not ashamed to say, I did my best to encourage her, still hoping against hope to dissuade my beloved from her fatal but dedicated interest in the parts of the highest emotional stress, or heaviest physical strain. While she was trying out Juliet's last lingering farewell, or

Miranda's lovely innocence, I gave Mrs. Plumstead every opportunity to recall:

' "You should have seen the sword combat in the *Dumb Ward of Genoa*. D'you know, Mr. Yallop, it had to keep time with the music! I'm not all in favour of letting the music rule any performance, but I must say that when Mr. Matthews added his song 'Bang up' to the 'Road to ruin' it was very popular. After all, what is a player doing if he doesn't hold the attention of his audience?"

'Could I, by inducing and elaborating the themes that Mrs. Plumstead was so familiar with, induce Sophia to see the shady, seamy side of the life, that for every spellbound moment when she might thrill an audience with one of her great speeches, delivered with her inimitable grace, there must always be not only days, but weeks of tedious preparation, exhausting rehearsal, insulting approaches from those who considered any female member of a theatrical company fair game . . .'

My uncle paused. His spirit became as it were clogged, with the growing bitter anxieties which attached to his love for the beautiful and talented girl. I was careful not to interrupt the recall of all those feelings, and gradually I began to feel more clearly what he had felt, and to re-create the life he had lived in those passion-shadowed days.

I followed him thus:

'The season turned out to be more pleasant as regards the weather, and I was able to induce the ladies, on the days when Sophia was not due for rehearsal, to accompany me in a comfortable carriage on short, but, I felt, recuperative trips to the countryside. It was delightful to witness her animation, the healthy bloom which replaced the rather hectic flush which her exertions too often produced on her cheeks. She was capable of enjoying to the full the wood-

land air of the Stratton Strawless plantations, the revivify-
ing breezes of Cawston Heath, the sight of the handsome
establishments in which the nobility and gentry of the wide
and rich country resided. There were opportunities, when
my partner Mr. Dunham, who was indulgent enough, and
more inclined to smile at what he must have regarded as a
somewhat belated infatuation for anyone of my serious
attachment to trade, than to find fault, had some commission to be executed at one or the other of them. This enabled
me to visit Gunton Hall of the Suffields, Houghton of the
Walpoles and many others of the neighbouring establishments. Sometimes I left the ladies in our conveyance, if I
had business to transact and the family were in residence.
If they were not, the housekeepers and head domestics were
usually ready enough, indeed proud, to exhibit the handsome rooms and well appointed offices to be seen.'

I reflected that my great-uncle would be pleased enough,
no doubt, to find so many of the county seats still occupied,
though not kept up with quite the state that they must have
been in the days of which he was speaking. There was, of
course, Holkham, enormous and characteristic, still to be
seen, Melton Constable, much reduced from its former
splendour, but still beautiful, Heydon and Felbrigg, and, of
course, some like that of the Custances which have completely disappeared. Some that have become almost accidentally famous through incidents in the lives of their occu-
piers that he would hardly have imagined, Kimberley which
has given its name to a far more famous city through the
irrelevant chance that its owner happened to be Queen
Victoria's minister when Africa was in its early stage of
development.

I did not, however, interrupt my great-uncle's train of
thought and soon became aware of how much more in-

volved he was in an entirely different range of images. His voice seemed to strengthen, I could almost imagine that his eye kindled and his cheeks coloured, as he recalled the relatively happy interlude he had spent all too briefly with his beloved, and her attendant.

'I had, of course, another motive than merely to amuse and entertain. I hoped that she might find the comparatively pleasant and healthy excursion a preferable way of spending her time, not only in improving her health, but in realising that I was able and only too willing to afford her a kind of existence of which she had been starved. I tried again and again to insinuate that, if she would only determine to forsake, or even diminish her assiduous devotion to what she felt her duty, I could give her a whole range of interest and occupation, of which she was largely deprived, whenever Mr. Brunton designated her for a part in one or another of his productions.'

'Were you ever successful in opening up a real alternative to the dedication she felt possessed her for the life of the boards?' I put it in such terms, hoping that I was falling into the rhythm of my great-uncle's verisimilitude of a living memory, and I seemed to succeed.

'I used to flatter myself that her spontaneous and delicious pleasure in the spring weather, the clothing of the woods with their verdure, the mystery added to the long distance views, by their being only visible as vistas between impenetrable walls of greenery, meant that she must surely conclude that the artificial light, the false exaltation of the proscenium view of life, the desolate, nerve-exhausting waiting and intervals, the jerk to the heart of the sudden call of a dramatic situation that must be exploited to the full, the fatigue of exertion on insufficient and unsuitably timed nourishment, were all well lost in exchange for a world of simple pleasures of the eye and ear. I hoped that the opportunities for repose, or for interest in the comfortable and satisfying chances I was able to extend to her, might, at long last, induce her to listen to the pleading I so manfully restrained. I assure you, Nephew, I did not weary her by importunity or repetition of my plea. I tried my best to let my intention lie concealed. I sometimes hoped I succeeded. I can hear now her rapturous exclamations:

' "Oh, John, look, can that be a squirrel? Oh, what a darling. I wish you could catch it."

' "My dear, I should need the skill of a steeple-jack, the persistence of a collector of the creatures of natural history. I will try if you like."

'I would make, I fear, half-hearted motions, descending from our vehicle and advancing towards the trees on which the agile animal found an easy retreat from the sound of our voices and the gestures of her pretty hands. This would soon show her the actual risk of what she asked and she would give vent to delicious little cries and motions to restrain me, even appeals to the highly amused if somnolent Mrs. Plumstead.

' "Oh, stop him! Oh, John, you mustn't. It makes me quite dizzy to see the little creature. I did want it for a pet, but you must not, must not, undertake any dangerous adventures for my sake!"

' "We might see if one of the village boys hasn't got a tame squirrel, or some other small creature you may fancy for a pet," interjected the sensible and countrified Mrs. Plumstead, "Mr. Yallop wouldn't do anything foolish, I am sure!"

' "No, he's nice and reliable," Sophia would agree, not without a move of pretended disappointment, but laying her hand on my arm to show appreciation.'

5

The Career

ABOUT this time I had leisure and opportunity to make some small research into the known facts of my great-uncle's life, its quiet provincial worthiness, only broken by his period of training in London, and the all-absorbing passion that besieged him there, and on his return home, finally by the death of Sophia Goddard.

What I found seemed to me to justify the fanciful reconstruction I had made of his earlier days (or that he made for me, I prefer to feel). Increasingly, as I glanced in passing at the portrait, or when no one was likely to challenge me:

'Whatever are you idling for, in that chair?'

I seemed to see a spark of life kindle in that kindly eye, a flush of deep feeling tinge that regular cheek and firm reticent mouth. More or less consciously I tried to meet him half-way along the tenuous bridge that seemed to give us access, one to another. I felt he wanted my understanding and sympathy, and the actual facts I was able to unearth seemed to justify what I thought must have been his state of mind. This was rendered easier by the sombre background against which Sophia Goddard's brief brilliant success in Norwich was enacted. He and she stood out all the more clearly, because, behind them, the 'total' war up to that date was ravaging the continent of Europe, isolating

Great Britain, and anyone regarding superficially the end of the eighteenth century and the opening of the nineteenth might be excused for saying:

'It was a time of dreary oppression, and our country was against revolution and new ideas, and associated with reaction and the holding down of the first overseas dominions in America and Asia!'

The real background of John Yallop and Sophia Goddard was full of great rolling clouds of conflict and crisis, and making all allowance for the fact that periods of history do not exactly symmetrically repeat each other, if we accept Wellington as the central figure, the Churchill of those years, I have been living recently through very similar emotions to those my great-uncle and his beloved might have exhibited, had not mere lapse of time and interval of distance prevented them.

While history was being made, half-way round the world, all that Norwich knew was the scarcity and annoyance that one finds pictured in Parson Woodforde's diaries. The war years were marked, not by aerial bombing and submarine blockade, but by great horse and cattle fairs, the occasional passage of troops through the streets or warships in Yarmouth roads. Not a bit of it. The event that Norwich held far more important would be the Assizes.

The Judge, then as now, represented the sovereign of the realm, on tour. The county families having for the time being closed the hunting and coursing seasons, and not yet contemplating that of the autumn shooting, would come in to occupy their City houses, Astleys and Wodehouses, Howards and Walpoles, Cokes and Straceys. The streets would be lined with cheering crowds, the Sheriff's coach would carry the Judge from his lodgings in Judge's Walk to the Guildhall for the City, and the Castle

for the County. Courts were preceded by uniformed trum-
peters and escorted by javelin men. There would be a ball
at the Assembly House, a sermon in the Presbytery of the
Cathedral. The garrison might parade, Lords Lieutenants
and High Stewards would be pointed out to visitors as they
carried on their varied functions. And for all the lesser
citizens there would be streets ankle deep in horse- and
cattle-droppings, shops displaying the latest London fashions, a concert of instrumental music, and perhaps the
greatest attraction of all, a public execution when as many as
half-a-dozen pitiable wretches would be strung up at the
foot of the bridge over the Castle Moat, for crimes as common and as reprehensible as sheep-stealing, holding-up the
Bury St. Edmunds coach, or a wretched girl's theft of a
bunch of ribands. But, more than anyone else, Mr. John
Brunton of the Theatre Royal would be busy putting on a
performance that stood a better chance of liberal patronage
than at any other time of the year.

With all this in mind, I stared at the portrait of my great-
uncle, closed my eyes, secure for the moment from interruption and tried to imagine his thoughts as the important
occasion approached.

Sophia might well have become slightly evasive. In reply
to his proposition that they might spend his free afternoon,
if it chanced to coincide with one when she was at liberty,
in driving over to Ranworth, on the Broads, and witnessing
the action of a decoy, which would snare a number of wild-
fowl to provide variety among the dishes to be set before
the company, at the banquet in the Maid's Head Hotel, I
thought I knew how he must have felt when, with this delightful project on the tip of his tongue, he called at Mrs.
Curtis's lodging and asked if he might see the lovely girl
who, he so eagerly hoped, would listen to his pleading and

allow him to charge himself with her well-being.

I thought I caught in my great-uncle's expression something of the disappointment he must have felt, when the good Mrs. Curtis replied with the quizzical air that all such women lend to any announcement of young people 'walking out', and a shake of the head : 'She've been up there', with a gesture of the whole of her shoulders that might vaguely indicate the general direction of the Theatre Royal, 'all the morning'.

'She didn't leave any message?'

'Not she.' Mrs. Curtis was not to be defrauded of any possible amusement frustration could cause.

'Did she say when she would be back.'

'You know what she is!' This would be directed to stir in such a nice young man, the reflection that he only wished he did know more about his beloved's movements. He was all too young to have sounded the depth of any woman's evasiveness, at once her protection and her habit of life. He had sense enough not to show any umbrage, for he must at all costs keep on the right side of Mrs. Curtis, who could, if offended, put all sorts of obstacles in the way of the meetings that shed upon his days the warmth and glamour of the sunshine and whose prevention would cast so deep a shadow.

'Oh, very well, thank you. I may be passing that way, this morning.'

'I shouldn't be surprised if you were,' was Mrs. Curtis's passing shot. To which she added, 'Mrs. Plumstead's out shopping. You wouldn't want to wait until she gets back?'

'Oh, I won't trouble her, thank you.'

'No, I shouldn't,' Mrs. Curtis did not wink. She was too kind a woman, and in her heart had long characterised

John and Sophia as 'Pretty dears. Does you good to see 'em. All innocent like.'

From what I was able to piece together, from my own intuitions and such rare mention of Sophia as occurred in the *Norwich Mercury* and other prints in which her name appeared, I had very little doubt that my great-uncle went straight to the Theatre, and gave a nod to old Fiddament, at the stage door, and entered.

I could easily reconstruct what he found there. The same atmosphere of dust and temporary disorder, of properties and scenery roughly stacked, not so much where it might be easy to find them, as the place in which it had been quickest to fling them aside as the stage manager, whom we should probably call 'producer' nowadays, had one of his almost continual inspirations and needed a change of scene, an interpolation or a cut in the written script. I could well imagine him, careful to keep out of sight and above all, out of the path of the busy stage hands, for however much a member of the cast may be willing to be seen in action by those he or she likes to characterise as 'their public', the men who have to manhandle the set-up, the lighting and the effects, are under no delusion that they are there to be looked at, and make short work of displacing anyone they find in their way.

He must have listened from some corner where he found refuge, and heard voices, with the particular lilt which is lent them by the necessity to throw the words with the right emphasis or hidden aside, into the farther corner of the auditorium. He must have winced at the sudden cleavage of another voice, speaking not into the void beyond the footlights, with its bitter edginess:

'Not like that! Not like that. For God's sake try and get the feeling of the scene!'

I

There would be, in some cases, three or four repetitions before the manager would be satisfied, but that would have been little comfort for my great-uncle, who, instead of the illusion that every interruption and repetition brought nearer the end of the rehearsal and the moment he might hope to meet her he had come to seek, had to submit to the other illusion, as the lines rolled forth from an actor or actress doing what the manager wanted. The illusion then became that the rehearsal would go on for ever, and never, never cease until the hour arrived for the curtain to go up, disclosing a make-believe Venice, an improbable Padua, or a Mantua such as Norwich could never provide, but which had to be superimposed on the restricted dimensions of Thomas Ivory's Theatre Royal; while outside the chilly, generally damp, but rarely extreme climate of the capital of East Anglia, would filter in through a dozen doors that could never close, or at least were never closed, making Nerissa or even Portia in her assumed robes, shiver, while old Shylock would be thankful for such protection as his beard might afford.

'At last, at last,' my great-uncle after heaven knows what disappointments, long-drawn-out intervals, arguments and repetitions, might say. 'I know that voice,' he might hug himself as he listened. Many notes higher than those of the male character, a thread of sweet purity would pour in the upper register, as Sophia took her cue and pronounced her lines. I wonder if he noticed at all, he may have been too bemused by mere proximity, such as back stage permitted him, the ominous hollow depth of some note of her voice. I wonder if he drew any sinister conclusion. Probably not! Had he known he was listening to a beauty that was doomed, the exhalation of lungs already diminished by the fatal encroachment of disease?

However, human beings seldom die of impatience unbelievably provoked. The hour did come when Mr. John Brunton, at the end of a scene which he would not admit to have satisfied him, for his standards were high, would at last grudgingly declare that he must turn to some other item in the performance, and with a threatening command:

'Well, there it is; that will have to do. All be back at two-thirty, and for heaven's sake take your parts with you, and don't let me catch any of you stricken dumb or paralysed this afternoon when you have the best chance of the year of making some impression on the public!'

I can well imagine the eager but humble waiting of my great-uncle, until Sophia came hurrying off the stage, her face earnest and thoughtful, becoming well the robes she had been wearing. I should not be surprised, if only we had any record of the times and conditions of rehearsals, if his outstretched hands and kindling glance were met by a gentle but firm denial, a preoccupied: 'Oh, it's you, John!' as she hurried him along the passage and allowed him the entry to her dressing-room. A less controlled or less well-intentioned lover might have ventured some word of reproach, complaining of the long waiting, or demanding some apology.

I do not think, from what little we know, that he allowed ill-temper to show. I expect he was all solicitous for her comfort, and offered, while she and her dresser were discarding her costume and cleaning off her make-up, to run out and find a hackney coach, so that she was comfortably and quickly conveyed to the table Mrs. Curtis had laid for her.

Once she was seated beside him scuttling over the cobbles of White Hart Lane and the Fish Market, I doubt if he could contain himself longer and I expect he was about to make some attempt to persuade her to tell Mr. Brunton of her intention to take no other parts, until she was, as her lover would put it, 'Fully recovered!'

I expect that the utmost reward he got for his abstention from disturbing questions was a warm pressure of the hand, a summoning of her gaze from contemplation of a remote and impossibly perfect rendering of her lines, as she realised that he had been listening and waiting for the best part of two hours.

'Dear John!' she might have allowed herself to breathe in his ear, 'were you really listening all the casket scene?'

But I suspect that she could not concentrate on his devotion for more than a moment, and that she was soon demanding:

'Tell me, was I in voice today? The drops Dr. Lubbock gave me are wonderful, but I fear that, while they keep my cough in check, they decrease the resonance of tone I try so hard to cultivate.'

Of course I do not know what he replied, and I think he was repulsed by the fact that the utmost solicitude he could display for her comfort, did not make the slightest breach in her absorption with her stage career. I have no doubt, that with no thought for himself, he confided her to the care of Mrs. Curtis, heard with dismay the good landlady complain:

'Well, I kept that nice and hot for you, never knowing when you would be in. Mrs. Plumstead had hers. She couldn't wait. She's gone to have her little nod,' which was probably Mrs. Curtis's fashion of describing Mrs. Plumstead's after dinner nap. I have no doubt that he heard with something like alarm:

'I don't want to disturb Mrs. Plumstead, I'm glad she didn't wait. And I can't eat all this. I've got to work ...'

and here I dare say, at the sight of Mrs. Curtis's face expressing the woman's doubt as to whether anything that took place on the stage could possibly be described as 'work', the light-hearted girl would burst out laughing.

I do not think my great-uncle did. This can only have been one of the many occasions on which his determination to save her health and life from the inroads that he felt, rightly enough, her career was making upon them was sidetracked and postponed, for she was preoccupied with other matters that seemed to her all important.

'You notice, John, that I've had an advancement!' When he looked blank, she put on a pretty *moue* and added:

'I did think you would have noticed.'

'Do you mean that Mr. Brunton is going to give you a rest, and find someone else to play these inferior small parts he gives you because you are uncomplaining?'

'Really, John, I wonder if the things you sometimes say to me can be spoken by the same man to whom I allow some degree of sensibility!'

Here she may have treated him to a frown of mock severity.

'My dear,' I feel sure he expostulated ... but she would not let him finish:

'You heard me rehearsing this morning. You don't mean to say that you did not recognise the lines?'

'I thought they were those spoken by Portia, in the *Merchant*.'

'That's better, but you are still not completely forgiven.'

'What have I said, or not said?'

'Don't you know ... no, perhaps you don't, and it is a shame to blame you, you can't feel as I do!'

Still mystified, I expect my great-uncle put on his best

manners and sought to discover where he had failed in comprehension.

She would lift her hand, and instruct him, in the very mood of the casket scene, with upheld finger.

'To play Portia is not often given to players of my years. The last time it was seen here, Mrs. Siddons . . .' Her voice rose, her eyes sparkled. Like any younger practitioner of the art, she loved to be mentioned in the same breath as the great actress. '. . . undertook the rôle. Now do you understand?'

'Dimly, my dearest. You have been promoted. You are no longer classed by Mr. Brunton as *ingénue*!'

'There. I knew you were more intelligent than you sometimes like to pretend.'

'My dear, I am all abasement and contrition.'

'You needn't kneel, on Mrs. Curtis's well-brushed carpet even. Your next line is to ask me, How do I know, I am sure?'

'I should not dream of doubting!'

'But you may, for I can confute your doubts with yet another piece of news, that follows!'

'Oh, do tell me!' I expect he was still hoping against hope, that she would announce some relaxation of the strenuous stage life she was leading. She soon undeceived him for she was not malicious, and the half of her that was not fully absorbed by her career, did, we know, value his attachment and enjoy his care of her and attention to her well-being.

'You'd never guess.' At the look on his face which she perhaps did not entirely fathom she added: 'No. It isn't fair to expect it. I'll tell you. Mr. Brunton is arranging his Benefit night for the end of the month. The 14th Light Dragoons are taking all the dress circle. He is putting on

Bluebeard and the Lying Valet ... Now perhaps you can guess what I am driving at!'

But I rather think my great-uncle was so bent on his own project, namely the implementing of their formal affiancing, and its announcement to the public, that would give him the right to defy even the 14th Light Dragoons, should they single her out as a toast, that he didn't at first see what she was hinting to him.

'Oh, John, I thought you admired Mr. Brunton's magnificent Moor of Venice.'

'I thought he was splendid in that exacting part.'

'Well then. Whom did he choose to play Desdemona?'

'Why, my dear, I remember the thrill I experienced when I saw you follow that heroine's tragic end.'

'John, you are really very dense. Are you sure that the Desdemona you saw wasn't Mrs. Rivett, or Mrs. Chestnut, or Mrs. Dwyer?'

'Why, my darling, of course not. The Desdemona I saw was played by you!'

'Quite right. And I played opposite Mr. Brunton.'

'Yes, dear, of course!'

'And Mr. Brunton's Benefit is fixed for the end of the month.'

'So you have just told me.'

'Then whose Benefit do you suppose will be billed next?'

'Why ... Can it be yours?'

'John, dear, you are not at your best this morning!' I feel sure she visited him with some such reproof, and she was nearer to the truth than she realised, or if she did, she was unwilling to admit it. He was in a profound puzzle as to know how to bring her round to the subject which was nearest his heart. Instead of that, she was moving further and further away into a world in which she would be famous, or at least deserved to be, and in which betrothed, not to say married life with him was a secondary if pleasant enough, but remote accompaniment.

'Then I shall have to tell you, but I don't like it. I do not boast I hope. You should have said the word for me.'

'Any word I can say, my dearest, you know . . .'

'I know you haven't said it. After the Benefit for Mr. Brunton, on the fourth May, he has fixed . . . now's your chance?'

'Could it be yours, as I suggested just now?'

'Yes it could, John. You may kiss me—that is, if you want to, after showing such reluctance to guess my good news!'

I do not think we need doubt his response, nor try to share with him the effort to appear as pleased as she felt he ought when the news sank like lead into his apprehensive heart. However, she had forgiven him, almost before the mild exhibition of his affection which was all she allowed, had at least made him conceal and postpone the topic which he was most anxious to discuss with her. She took advantage of this and began to describe, I feel sure, the announcement soon to be made public in the newspaper, the *Norwich Mercury,* following that of Mr. Brunton's own occasion, of Miss Goddard's Benefit.

'He's putting on a comedy and a farce for me. And, what do you think, John?'

John couldn't think; I am confident, shrank from it.

'He has a piece entitled *Incle,* by Yarica, which gives me a chance to sing a duet with Mrs. Dwyer. That ought to be a success! I like being helped out by the music. And Mrs. Dwyer is so good. Then he's going to put on the *Belle's Stratagem.* It's so well known, it is sure to please, the cheap seats can nearly say the words themselves. There's an item too, of a minuet, that Mrs. Chestnut will dance with me. And then, to wind up, the *Road to Ruin*, where I have the name part of Sophia. Mr. Phillips and Mrs. Dwyer are playing to help me. Isn't that lovely?'

I have no doubt that my great-uncle did his very best to look interested and to assure her that he was confident of her success. I expect she was a magnificent sight, justifying the looks the miniaturist was to immortalise and which tell us today that John Yallop was no fool. Any man might fall in love with Sophia Goddard and no doubt many did, or were at least stage struck by her bearing and her vocal and graceful accomplishments, when she sang her duet and danced the minuet laid down for her.

There is little that we can know for certain about that and many a day that must have followed a similar course. Meanwhile, John Yallop was more concerned . . . (did he insist on her being treated by Dr. Lubbock?) . . . with her health, and his prudent and very proper plan for safeguarding it was to diminish her efforts at the Theatre, and to constrain her to live a more normal and less wearing life as his wife, whenever he could induce her to make effective the engagement he had at some time prevailed upon her to enter into. Many an affectionate if humorous aside did he have to submit to, from his parents, his partner and his friends:

'Well, John dear, you have made a most fascinating choice,' I have no doubt his doting mother told him when he took Sophia to his parents' home. 'But when is it to be? You know we are only too glad to welcome Miss Goddard whenever she is free to come. But she is so occupied with her theatrical career.' What could my great-uncle reply? He was only too anxious to bring Sophia more and more into the steady and regular life over the glover's shop on the

Gentleman's Walk, where his parents kept their unobtrusive but comfortable home.

His father would adopt a more bluff and jocular attitude:

'Well, young feller, when is it to be? The girl's a nice one, and very popular I see by the notice she gets in the *Mercury*. Don't be shy about it.'

What could he say? He wasn't shy. He had nothing to conceal. He had offered the beautiful girl a home, maintained by the flourishing business he conducted with Mr. Dunham. He could offer not only that, but, had she ever demanded it, he could submit for her choice no mean display of rings and jewels. One can hear him trying to induce her, quite innocently, to make selection:

'Ruby would become you well, or Sapphire. Some say emeralds are lucky. Pearls, if you like, or diamonds, but I might not be able to obtain so high a quality, in the very precious stones!'

I have no doubt that she let her glance, that could charm an audience or repel a dishonest approach, light up at the sight of the beautiful things he was able to display. Ruby and emerald, he might be right, would enhance her dark beauty. We do not know if she were superstitious, as many of her calling are, not without excuse, when one considers the risks they run, the fickle nature of public applause, the false values lent to the most correct performance by the mere fact that it is a performance, the invitation of an individual to concentrate how many pairs of eyes and ears on the figure and voice of one.

'No, John, no, not opals. Don't you know they are unlucky?'

'There are all sorts of silly tales about what it is fortunate or unfortunate to wear, my dearest. Here am I who live by the traffic of these goods. I have not suffered from any infection they have left on my hands. If one or other of them were to please you, surely that is a quality that produces happiness, and that is the object of human life, isn't it? So I was always taught at the Meeting House my parents attended and to which I accompanied them.'

Sophia would always listen attentively, would even allow her hand to rest in his when he spoke so, but like many another man he found himself confronted by a resistance, so passive, so apparently yielding, that it took him long to learn that it was formidable, perhaps all the more formidable, because it was conditioned by affection, and susceptible of persuasion, at least on the surface, seldom further.

'Yes John,' I expect she said. 'Happiness is a precious boon. I love to think that I have the power, or so the audience I draw seem to think, to dispense it. But I should never succeed if I did not feel I was giving something of myself!'

That of course alarmed him. It was just what he feared, what Dr. Lubbock diagnosed, and Mrs. Curtis in her homely but shrewd innocence foretold. When he begged her to let him know which of the goods he so temptingly deployed would please her best, she might end by giving him some small nod or touch of approval and then say:

'They are all lovely. Somehow I don't like to separate them. They enhance each other. Let me have a plain gold circlet. It is honest and undying!'

Once again he suppressed a shudder, for it seemed she was deliberately inviting and preparing for a demise that would render necessary a tribute that would outlast her mortal frame. That was winning indeed, but he, manlike, wanted her here and now, in the Norwich of the last year of the eighteenth century.

So there was aroused between them a loving but fatal

contention. Though they never defined it in words, he grew
to know as the weeks passed that he must always find himself induced into that path of argument that always ended
and must end in what to him was the abyss. In vain he had
listened to Dr. Enfield, who, sensible, rational and never
extreme had led him to accept the simple tolerant belief of
the Meeting House, that those who loved faithfully and
well could never be separated, but must be forever joined
in a marriage not of this world.

She never refused him a clasp of the hand, a supporting
embrace of arm or shoulder, and from time to time re-
warded him with the liberty of her lips. But he was always
left with the impression that she deliberately paid what she
felt she owed his steadfastness, and was all the time peering
past him, to that visionary moment of exaltation, applause,
and encore, when she would bring some one or other of the
scenes in which she appeared to a triumphant conclusion.

But too often, those moments of triumph were not his.
They were exchanged between her and 'her public'. They
ended too often in a portraying of death. And sure enough,
they culminated in the descent of the curtain, and the end
of that brilliant, frail, foredoomed moment of stage success.
If he had been allowed 'behind' to welcome her when her
second or third appearance before the curtain had terminated in uproar, the stamping of feet and the chorus of
shouting, the noise would all die away and he would offer
his arm to lead her down the grimy passage to her dressing-
room. He would press her arm against him and murmur his
own small praise, as she languidly, almost fainting, would
allow herself to be screened from any onlookers in the privacy into which he and her dresser, and sometimes Mrs.
Plumstead were alone allowed to penetrate. Often she would
sink in the chair before her mirror and bend like some ten-

der tree before the gusts of coughing and breathlessness that threatened to overwhelm her. Soon she would heroically master them and demand, hoarse and gasping as she was:

'John, dear, was I really good that time? Did you feel the shudder I put into it?'

Or it might be: 'Did I fall back too soon, and did I give Mr. Brunton time to say the concluding line before they started applauding?'

Of course he must have reassured her scores of times. This needed no feigning on his part, the auditorium might well still be ringing with the demand that she should appear again and take one more bow. And Mr. Brunton, sensibly enough, would sign to the enthusiastic benches and boxes, that the performance must close. Or, if her part was to be followed by a farce or pantomime, a song or dance from one of the other members of the company, that the next item must now proceed.

How often I longed to have been present at one of those evenings, or even a matinée of a century and a half ago. I would have put up with the obtrusive attempts of the young officers of the garrison, or the members of one or other of the county families to invade her privacy in order to have heard how my great-uncle comforted the exhausted girl, and was presently allowed to lead her away, her costume discarded for her own clothes, her burning cheeks, and skilfully touched eyes and lips cleansed of her make-up, to the hackney coach I have no doubt he provided if it were inclement weather. While I could almost hear him when I interrogated my great-uncle's portrait, I could never catch any implied denial in that steady front he made to whoever looked at him. I suspect he reassured her, telling her how much he had enjoyed her Juliet, her Desdemona, or her Ophelia. Her Maria in *The Citizen* seems to have been as often called for, to judge by the frequency with which this piece was played, or her Lady Teazle when she was allowed to understudy Mrs. Brunton, who was, after all, her senior in the company at the Theatre Royal, and the wife of the manager. My great-uncle, who was a magistrate, must have been obliged to attend in a box, during Assize week, and I have always fancied that something shows in his portrait, a background of seriousness, almost of pathos, and I have often mentally demanded of him, when I felt most intimate with his image:

'Great-Uncle, didn't you suffer agonies, when you saw her, exposed to the public survey, heard her discussed by the young bloods, or even by members of the company who were, not without reason, rather piqued that so young a performer, and so recent an addition to the Norwich stock company should receive such flattering notice in the *Mercury* newspaper and was asked, on all sides, to lend her abilities to make a success of the Benefits accorded to her fellow players?'

I felt he replied to me as plainly as if he had spoken: 'She was as generous as she was fair. She not only put up with my parents' kindly, but sometimes ill-judged, assertions that she would be much better off as my wife than she could ever be "with all this play-acting" as my worthy but none too tactful father would put it. Of course he loved her, what male creature could ever resist her charm!'

'None whatever, Great-Uncle, I myself, you must have heard me admire her miniature.'

'And well you might, Nephew. I have gazed at it myself for long moments almost imploring it to come to life and speak to me. But you see, she was born to be admired, had no need, and has never since she died had any means of more or less verbal communication, such as you now lend me!'

'I am only too proud, Great-Uncle. What more can any-one have than admiration and affection in this life, and to be lamented when one has passed on!'

'She certainly had that, Nephew, for not only were my homely parents anxious to see more of her and that I should have her undivided attention, but there are the names and facts, plain enough in the records of the time. Again and again she was asked to help all the other members of the company.'

'I know what the Bruntons took for their Benefit from *The Merchant of Venice*. That was her Portia.'

'No. I think Mrs. Brunton played Portia, and Sophia had to be content with Nerissa, and the chance of understudying Portia, if Mrs. Brunton was tired or indisposed. Then came her own Benefit, her Incle and Yarico duet, and her minuet with Mrs. Chestnut!'

'I wonder what Mrs. Chestnut received for her sup-port?'

'From the records, Nephew, I rather fancy she was only too glad to be associated with Sophia whom many of the company must have come to regard as a rising star. Mrs. Chestnut may well have had a family of children in the background, and have been only too glad to stand in with so prominent a performer.'

'That was the occasion when she played the name part of Sophia in *The Road to Ruin*.'

'Anyhow, Nephew, my darling helped her to obtain so much. The boxes were extended over part of the Pit, I re-member. Phillips and Sophia had a duet and the perform-ance wound up with *Bluebeard* played as a panto!'

'Surely, Uncle, if they could play her as Juliet and Des-

demona, they did not include her with Harlequin and Punch
and the string of sausages?'

'No, they did not, but Brunton may have put his foot
down. He was a man of good taste and decision, who
would have seen that there was no danger in letting her be
surrounded by incongruous associations.'

Here my uncle broke off, and the portrait glowed with
the trick of the light or it may have been with the long-
buried emotions that we sometimes feel.

'I recollect one of those chilly May mornings when the
crowd which had assembled for the Assizes was beginning
to disperse, how I went to the Theatre to offer to see her
home, for one never knew to what unwelcome advances
she might not be subjected while the excitement of the occasion lasted. She met me with what I was beginning to fear
was a permanent state of excitement. In Mrs. Curtis's par-
lour she seized both my hands and held me before her, as
she had held so many of the stage lovers that her wide
repertoire brought her.

' "John dear, what do you think?"

'Of course I was quite incapable of thought, confronted
by that vision, and remained tongue tied:

' "Mr. Brunton has given me the result of my Benefit.
Guess how much!"

'I am afraid I allowed my constant guessing powers to
show in my face for she shook me severely.

' "Come, speak up!" in her firm "stand up and deliver"
voice.

'As I failed to find words, she flung me from her with an
adorable gesture of impatience, groped on the table behind her, and turning, as she had been trained to do, so as
to show her profile and the outline of her figure to so many
audiences, she whipped out a bag, and let its contents of

golden sovereigns cascade upon the cloth.

' "There!" she insisted, "what do you think of that?"

'Of course I sought her hands, outstretched thus, and clasped them to me. Then I hurriedly gathered up the pile of coins, and scooped it back into the bag from which it had come. Then I did manage to stumble out some feeble word of congratulation, as I held her before me, her eyes dancing with provocation, her delicate complexion flushed, as the application of her make-up never shaded it so delicately.

' "Yes, isn't it delightful? It means that the public do really like my presentation of the parts. And Mr. Brunton is very complimentary, and Mrs. Brunton most generous in her praises. I really think they will not refuse me anything I ask . . . in reason of course. Oh, I am so happy!"

'Nephew, I tried to join in her innocent spontaneous delight. But it was hard work, for my heart beat with but a leaden chime to her gay sortie. I foresaw that this outstanding success would render it all the harder to wean her from her impassioned love of the theatre, her mounting ambition to climb to even greater success, and the fell consequences I feared only too clearly. Of course I tried:

' "Well, darling, now that you see you have had already as much fame as anyone of your years can possibly expect, won't you rest awhile and allow me to take the position you know I am so anxious to fill? My parents keep asking when they may expect to welcome you not merely as an admired artiste in the profession you have conquered, but as a daughter-in-law they will love to cherish. Won't the end of this season be a suitable time for us to make the announcement? I feel sure Mr. Brunton would be only too glad to entice you back, once he has seen how much his company loses by an even temporary absence of yours from the place you fill?"

K

'It was painful in the extreme to see the happy smile fade from her features. She drew a little apart from me and I saw that I was once more faced with one of those evasions at which she was so adept:

' "John dear," she said, and her tone had dropped from the high delighted pitch of a moment before: "What you say is very sweet, and you know that your affection is dearer to me than any applause from even a larger audience. But you are not so mean, I well know, as to grudge the same sort of pleasure that I have just been given, to those who are not so fortunate as myself?"

'I wondered for the moment to whom she could be referring in this cunningly invented obstacle to all my dearest wishes. She went on:

' "You would not have me ungrateful, I know. I owe at least some measure of my good fortune to Mr. and Mrs. Chestnut. They have a smaller share of the profit than mine and they are needy and hard put to it, while I can always throw myself on your loving shoulders. I must work hard to repay Mrs. Chestnut for her part in the minuet she danced with me and which you heard so much applauded!"

'Of course, Nephew, I could but acquiesce. Mrs. Chestnut was a sturdy creature, like one of the female players Hogarth has pictured. My own opinion was that she was glad enough to be allowed to share an item with Sophia, whose grace and aristocratic bearing gained, I must admit, a certain refinement by contrast with her fellow players. So I remained silent and forbidden, but my dear love went on, with all the more excitement:

' "Then there was Mr. Phillips' song ... the Hawking Song that is always so popular. His Benefit follows close on the Chestnuts'. I would be ashamed not to do my very best in return for what he did for me with his vocal item.

And he wrote for me my Occasional Address that I spoke at the conclusion. Of course Mr. Brunton is putting on *Bluebeard* again for him, because the pantomime takes so well with the public to whom the Phillipses and the Chestnuts appeal."

'I leaned by the window, trying to answer her sweet and generous looks, with all the admiration I could not help feeling, but she was by this time so excited that I could not interrupt:

' "You have seen that they extended the boxes over part of the Pit for me, but Mr. Brunton will have the false floor removed to make all the more room for the supporters of my friends. I shall sing a duet with Mr. Phillips, and it was pathetic to see the gratitude of his poor wife. I really can't think how they will bring up all those children." She broke off:

' "Do you know, John, I sometimes feel quite guilty when I compare my good fortune with the lives of drudgery that so many have to lead!"

'You will believe, Nephew, that I was deeply touched by the feeling she showed for those doubtless excellent colleagues of hers, whom, I am afraid, I was only too ready to put down as sturdy but insignificant troopers. I was more concerned at the moment by the severe fit of coughing that the too strong and too vehemently expressed feelings brought on. I induced her to take a seat by the fire and remonstrated as thoroughly as I dared:

' "You must see for yourself that you are quite unfit to add all this extra effort, and you ought to tell Mr. Brunton so!"

' "But my dear John," she took me up, "Mr. Brunton has quite enough on his hands. Do you know, while this very unspringlike weather continues, he has given an order for all the fires in the passages to be kept going. Now be a dear, instead of growing so apprehensive about my wretched chest, go to the shop near Gurney's Bank, and buy as many tickets for the Phillips' Benefit as you feel you can afford. Look, here is my portion . . ."

'And that golden-hearted creature, Nephew, reached out for her money bag and scooped up in her delicate hands as many gold pieces as they would hold:

'Of course I refused them.

' "Dearest heart!" I adjured her, "I will do as you say, and if I should meet Mr. Phillips, I shall praise his item and tell him how much he owes to you, and what you were prepared to do for him!"

'She mastered her cough, and was able to smile at me through the moisture her heaving chest had lent to her eyes, so that they glistened like diamonds of the first water, all too brilliantly I feared, and I was dismayed to hear her continue:

' "Then you can also go to Stevenson & Matchett and buy tickets for the Dwyers' Benefit, which Mr. Brunton has fixed for the eighth. He is putting on *The Chapter of Accidents* and has summoned Mrs. Dwyer from the place she has filled so admirably in the company at Windsor. There's devotion for you! I can hardly do less when she does so much!"

'I tried my hardest to show my concern for Dwyer's excellent wife, who, it is true, must have had a very fatiguing week, travelling from the Thames Valley to take part with her husband. I had not heard this news, and feared it would only be used as a further excuse for demands upon Sophia's frail strength, and the energy she gave so recklessly to the aid of others. She was full of it:

' "Mr. Dwyer will sing the Hunting Song from *Mah-*

moud and they will wind up, not with a pantomime, but with that piece called *The Romp,* in which Mrs. Dwyer is so diverting as Priscilla."

'I had a deep suspicion, Nephew, that Mrs. Dwyer had begun life as an acrobat in some family circus such as Astley's, and that it had only been the passage of time, the paucity of circus stands, and the uncertainty of the life, that had enabled her, with sheer good fortune, to have a part in the Norwich stock company, and so perhaps to catch the eye of the manager of the company playing at Windsor. But I knew better than to suggest the faintest doubt as to the ability and charm of any of Sophia's fellow players, and attract her scornful defence of them when they were, partly through the effort she herself could so ill spare, to have some share in the Benefit performances Mr. Brunton was allowing his troupe.

'But I little knew how much that unselfish girl had mapped out for herself the arduous contribution she was determined to make to her companions' well-being. So I busied myself in picking up the coins she had recklessly scattered on the table, confident, I suppose, that she could always command more. I counted it into the leather pouch, and without daring to caution her as to the need to husband her resources, I volunteered to take charge of the money for her.

' "That will be safer, no doubt, but as I earned the money I think you might allow me to spend at least a few pounds of it on my necessities!"

'I manfully restrained myself, Nephew, from pointing out that if she would only yield to my loving and solicitous request, she would, as my wife, be amply provided, and not need to rely on the precarious success which had enabled Mr. Brunton to deal liberally with her on this occasion, but might just as likely cause him to think, at some date, perilously near, that he must keep a tight hold on the profits of the company's performances. And then I saw that she was still not thinking in the same terms as I, of a future which we should share together, I providing the wherewithal and she, if she still persisted in her longing for the life of the boards, the applause, the excitement and the severe limitations of that life, able to indulge her fancies as often or as seldom as she wished and even to refuse to act unless her health and inclination made it desirable. I had no idea what she was ruminating, when she turned suddenly upon me in her chair:

' "John, have your parents never asked to meet mine and make the acquaintance of members of my family with whom they will be related, once I surrender to the importunities you use to break down my resistance ...?"

'I did not know what to say. Mystified, I waited until she added:

' "It would be only natural that your family would ask what family I had. But, John, will they believe me when I say that I don't know!"

'I did not at first, Nephew, guess to what end the exquisite cunning of this turn of the subject was intended to lead. Of course I protested:

' "My dear, I have never made any inquiries. Since that first moment, when I met you in the passages to the dressing-rooms, at the Lane, and we recognised each other, and knew it was for life, I have hardly given the matter a thought. If you don't know of any relatives, all the better. You can come to me ..."

' "But that is not what I want you to say, John. I know well enough," she replied, "that I can rely on you. It's rather Mrs. Plumstead I am thinking of. Her career, to which she hardly alludes, and which must in any case now be ended, will leave her with no means of support that I know of. I would like to reward her for all the care she has taken of me since I was a young girl, and now I have at length the means of making her a substantial present."

'I saw clearly enough, Great-Nephew, that her Benefit, a substantial sum as such rewards go, would not last her long, and I was ready enough to assure her that I would provide for Mrs. Plumstead's future requirements, once we were married. But once again, she eluded all my advances before they had begun.

' "You see, John," she said, "I am no one in particular. Mrs. Plumstead only says, when I ask her, that we shall be provided for. She never says by whom or when. I would like her to feel able to shake herself free from the responsibility she and my various school mistresses have borne so faithfully all these years!"

'I forebore to interrupt and point out that in any case she was now only arriving at years of discretion, as it is called, or was in those days, but she was intent on her project of sharing some of her hard-won gains with her chaperone. I asked how much she felt would be adequate for her purpose and she said, let her have half, to give the excellent person who had indeed cared for her in her girlhood so faithfully. I little foresaw to what I was lending myself, for she continued as I counted out the sum:

' "That's a dear! The rest you can keep until next time."

' "Next time?" I inquired.

' "We don't know when I shall want to make some other provision."

' "But surely, my dear, once you leave the stage, I shall be allowed to make sufficient provision for anything Mrs. Plumstead may require."

' "No, John, you must forgive me if I say, you don't quite understand. I want Mrs. Plumstead to have something of mine, not of yours!"'

'It was so plain to me, Great-Nephew, that once we were married, my resources, already by no means contemptible would be at her disposal. But I soon found she had taken another view of herself. She was, so to say, a child of the theatre. Mrs. Plumstead was merely the protection that the manners of the time demanded. She did not grieve for the mother she had never known, still less for the father she was unlikely ever to identify. She felt herself a creation of that world of make-believe, in which I had first met her. From that view of herself had sprung her ability to recognise me at a glance, as the only person whose devotion she could accept and return in equal measure. I could scarcely quarrel with that attitude, and so I was obliged to leave her as she hastened to prepare for her part in the Dwyers' Benefit.

'Alas, had she even then listened to me or to her medical adviser, there might have been time to build up her overtaxed strength. But no sooner was the Dwyers' Benefit acted out, and they had received their share, than the Benefit of the Wheelers was billed. *The Road to Ruin* was put on, with Sophia in her usual part. It was, I felt as I witnessed the performance, a sorry affair, which did her no credit, though her item was most applauded. It was the sort of made-up theatrical programme, Nephew, in which somewhat stale dialogue is eked out with supposedly popular sentiment. Wheeler sang his song "The King and Constitution". His well-meaning wife played her well-known part in *The Ghost, or Dead Man Alive* and so forth.

'Once more I began to hope we were at the end of the exhausting season, and that she might obtain some repose.

Not a bit of it! Seymour claimed his turn, and I suppose
Mr. Brunton was obliged to give it him, rather than run the
risk of depleting the company. But, a week later, Sophia,
who had not been called upon, and had been allowed a
little respite while *Henry IV and the Humours of Sir John
Falstaff*, very properly described as a "Farce and Entertainment", agreed to play, once again, the name part in *Jane
Shore* for the unhandy Huddert. I did remonstrate that she
was over generous to those who could never repay her by
anything they could lend to her similar chances. But she
still stood in for the Chestnuts in *The Castle Spectre*, and
at the end of the month even Lindoe and Bartram had
their turn. I do not know under what obligation Mr. Brunton was obliged to favour those indifferent performers—
but in *The Stranger* Sophia took her usual part of Mrs.
Haller. Finally, and lastly, old Mrs. Rivett, in the box office,
had to demand her services as Maria. She even doubled
the part with Lady Bel.

6

The Victim

BY this time I began to obtain corroboration of the curious, half-dreamt, part meditated story that my great-uncle had, not so much told me, literally, as made me tell myself. With a little investigation at our Public Library, and the old Subscription Library of which he was a member, I found many files of the old fortnightly *Norwich Mercury* newspaper, and other publications, and was able to check the titles of the pieces in which Sophia Goddard played, in London and subsequently in Norwich, and often the parts allotted to her. I was able, therefore, to sympathise with him when he saw her expending her frail strength so generously to help out the Benefits of one after another of the members of the company. I could almost hear him say, as I sat gazing at the portrait, in which I now seemed to recognise a demeanour of sadness and apprehension:

'I little thought, when I heard that she was not playing in the *Winter's Tale*, which the Mayor and Mrs. Harvey had requested the new manager, Mr. Hindes, to put on, that I had seen her last appearance on that stage. I went at the earliest opportunity to Mrs. Curtis's house and was shocked at the long face the landlady drew, to receive me:

' "It's about time you came," she spoke as if I were at fault in not calling, when in fact I had restrained myself in the hope that Sophia was, at long last, taking a good rest and should be spared the excitement which I still longed to feel my visits would cause her, with their imploring of her to break off her stage engagements, and consider seriously an early date for our marriage.

' "Has she been asking for me?"

' "She's not one to complain, as you know," Mrs. Curtis rejoined as she closed the door behind me, "but she just looks and sighs when she isn't coughing!"

' "Then let me see her at once, please."

' "Come in!" was the rejoinder, and to my alarm, the landlady led the way upstairs. She stopped me at the door of the bedroom which looked out on to the garden, above the wall of which appeared against the sky, the tree-tops that earned for Norwich the title of the City of Gardens.

' "Hold you hard," I was enjoined, "while I see if she's asleep." I did, and was invited a moment later: "You can come in!" backed by a glance in which admiration was tinged with commiseration. "There she is, the poor dear," and Mrs. Curtis left us.

'Sophia had been helped by Mrs. Plumstead into a sitting position, a lace fichu had been draped over those dark curls, her cheeks were coloured by the fitful tint of fever, but her throat disclosed the perfect symmetry of all her limbs. Her whole being seemed to come looming up into her eyes, and she offered her hands, while Mrs. Plumstead put a chair to enable me to sit beside her bed, and reduce the effort of speech.

'Her voice, however, was lent the full touch that owed I do not know how much to the consummate artifice of which she was the mistress.

' "John, dear, I knew you would come!"

'I was cut to the heart by the implication of urgency. "I

only held back in order to let you have the greatest leisure and repose!"

' "You don't diminish my repose, John. I always feel the better for you!"

'Again that note of urgency!

' "I hear that you have had the good sense not to appear in Mr. Hindes' forthcoming production."

' "Isn't it a shame? I feel quite guilty. But Dr. Lubbock is very stern with me, John! He makes me lie here."

' "I am very glad to hear it!"

'She gave a stifled, protesting laugh.

' "Yes. I know you are. You don't realise that I am only half alive, like this."

'She gave a piteous glance at the outline of her poor recumbent limbs, outlined by the clothes. The words she used suggested the retort, "Better half alive than to lose life altogether," but I sternly repressed it and substituted.

' "He must know best what is good for you, my dear!"

' "I sincerely hope so. I want to be able to take part in *False Shame,* in March. And there are songs by Mr. Bennett and this Mr. Fisher."

' "My dear, is that wise?"

She gave vent again to the half-deprecating laugh that was one of the most adept turns of her acting:

' "No! Do I look wise, John, in this *déshabille*? Would you like me to wear a dunce's cap to show there is something else in life besides WISDOM?"

'She gave that word all the weight of her most sonorous tones, and set herself coughing. Mrs. Plumstead was assiduous in caring for her, and I drew back, fearing that her symptoms might only increase by the very fact of my presence, and the courageous front she was determined to put before me.

' "There," she declared as she mastered the fit, "that's what comes of staying in bed. I should be better up and about!"

'I glanced across at Mrs. Plumstead, who shook her head, and I put some show of authority into replying, "I hope you won't think of it!"

'This brought a tender and endearing submission: "I won't, John, if it pleases you!"

'What could I say in reply to that pseudo-meek tone, and upward glance that would have drawn plaudits from an audience, and how much more suppressed emotion from me?

'I was not to be let off with that, and she added with a fine show of irritation:

' "It's very dull, lying here!"

' "My dear, I see you have your books about you to pass the time."

' "I read until I am tired, John, and all the time I am longing to get up and deliver the words in the most forceful stance!"

' "My dear, just enjoy the appropriate phrases!"

'This roused her again:

' "If you say that, I'll jump out of bed and show you how they ought to be said."

' "Now, is that wise?"

' "You said that before. Don't repeat yourself, John." She wagged a finger at me.

' "It was well meant!"

' "My dear John, that is a mood that never goes over well. The public want something more than excellent intentions."

'I knew that was true. I could only answer:

' "The public is a hard task-master. You know that."

' "Not I! Most of the audiences to which I have played have been indulgence itself. Far more so than the critics."

' "The critics may well be envious, when you attract the applause they would prefer to see accorded to their favourites they have praised mistakenly."

' "It's sweet to hear you speak so, but my fellow members in the company are always so charitable, though many of them have years of experience longer than mine."

' "I am glad to hear it. You have been more than charitable to many of the less able, when you were so lavish in your backing of their Benefits. They must owe you pounds and pounds they never would have earned without your support."

'She gave a little sigh. I felt that even our conversation fatigued her, she seemed to realise my anxiety, and when I added, hoping to please her:

' "You can trace in those books many a line you have said as only you can say it. You must draw comfort from that."

' "Oh, I do. And when you come to see me, and speak so kindly, I remember playing Juliet. Here are the lines:"

'She drew herself up in bed and spoke in the alluring voice I had heard charm an uncouth audience:

' "If thou dost love, pronounce it faithfully,
    Or, if thou thinkest I am too quickly won
    I'll frown and be perverse and say thee nay
    So thou wilt woo! . . .

' "That just describes you, John. You are too besotted with this lazy lie-abed girl."

' "My dear, you know it is only for the good of your health."

' "Yes, I have heard that before. Poor little Juliet didn't have such a rebellious carcase as I seem to be plagued with."

' "My dear . . ." I protested.

' "Oh, I know what you're going to say. Here are the lines that reply:

> and therefore thou mayest think my
> 'haviour light.
> But trust me, gentleman, I'll prove more true . . ."

. . . here she broke off with a laugh.

' "I could parody those lines, John, and make them read: 'I'll prove in better health, 'ere long' "

' "That's what I want to hear. I'll make a bargain with you. Rest and recuperate, and as soon as you are fit for it, in Dr. Lubbock's eyes, I'll put in a request for *Romeo and Juliet,* and get some of the more influential citizens to back it. Perhaps Mr. Harvey could be induced . . . and then we'll see that Mr. Hindes finds you a Romeo worth while . . .'

' "That will be lovely, John. Oh how I long to play the part! Romeo has that swearing sequence, as we call it."

'Her voice came true and sweet as ever I had heard her, as she forgot her discomfort and the lassitude attending it:

> ' "Lady (he says) by yonder blessed moon I swear
> That tips with silver all those fruit tree-tops . . .

' "Why John, this is the very room. Look out of the window at the apple trees in the garden. The very scene!"

'She goes on:

> ' "O swear not by the moon, th' inconstant moon
>   That monthly changes in her circle orb,
>   Lest thy love prove likewise variable . . ."

' "My dear love," I interrupted, and leaning over I ran my finger down Romeo's speech:

' "What shall I swear by?"

' "Isn't that just what I've been pestering you with these many months. You do know that you have only to name the day, and you need never depend on re-learning those lines again!"

' "Yes. I know, John. But look how she takes him up!" And with raised hands she declaimed:

' "Do not swear at all; or if thou wilt, swear by thy
                                    gracious self
    Which is the god of my idolatry . . ."

'Here she broke off and turned to the patient Mrs. Plumstead who sat there, witnessing this interlude in the hours of careful nursing she must have endured.

' "I don't use such high-flown language about him, in real life, do I? He would get altogether too good an opinion of himself!"

'But I broke in to try to bring her thoughts back to my pet project:

' "Listen, dear, Shakespeare is all very well. But I am talking prose not poetry. When will you come to me?"

'Here she put on a mock-serious air and picked up the cue she wanted from the book:

' "Well, do not swear; Although I joy in thee,
    I have no joy of this contract to-night.
    It is too rash, too unadvised, too sudden,
    Too like the lightening, which does cease to be
    Ere one can say 'It lightens'."

'Here Mrs. Plumstead interposed:

' "That's a very good text. You know that Dr. Lubbock said he'd look in on his morning round. Now you're all worked up and I don't know what he'll say when he feels your pulse."

' "I do hope I haven't done more harm than good, Mrs. Plumstead," I felt bound to protest. "I hoped I could cheer her up."

' "I'm sure you didn't mean any harm, but I think she's had as much excitement as she can stand just now!"'

'This was obvious good sense and I was a little daunted to see that Sophia only made protest by an affectionate glance of submission to her guardian, and turned to me to hold out her hand to be kissed. As I moved to the door she gave me a long, long look and I had all I could do, Nephew, to hold back the tears that made my eyes smart.'

At this point I seemed to lose connection with my great-uncle. I do not know if it were some unknown influence that may affect that eerie look of a portrait of one long dead, but called to life by family affection, and I must confess some degree of curiosity to know how he had felt during those agonising months of Sophia's last illness. But it was some time before I was able to feel again that I was being allowed to follow his thoughts, and not only that, but his very footsteps, in his native city, a century and a half gone by.

First I seemed to see him passing along the Gentleman's Walk, and then as he came to Stevenson & Matchett, the booksellers, he caught sight of some publication in their window, and went in.

I caught him up, if that is how one should describe the queer process that enabled me, as I felt, to understand the thoughts, see the figure of my great-uncle against the back-

L

ground of the daily commerce of his time and even hear the words his lips would have said, had I been transferred back to him, or he in some way reproduced by my imagination.

He seemed to stop at the shop the management of which he shared with Mr. Dunham, as their advertisement showed in the *Norwich Mercury*. Already his new energy, or other qualities had begun to influence the development of the business. The announcements in the paper crammed between news of the Peace of Amiens, of other world events, the prospectuses of state lotteries, the pills and medicaments of those who proposed, at least, to cure a wide variety of ills and quoted lengthy testimonials from sufferers who had been relieved, spoke of Dunham and Yallop as having tea, coffee and cocoa for sale, furniture and even clothes, in addition to their original display of gold and silver objects, rings and ornaments, jewellery and valuables.

The picture clears a little. Has he settled some point with his partner, or given instructions to one or another of the employed staff, as we should call it today, the numbers of which must have been increased in order to deal with the expanding variety of classes of trade in which the firm was interested? I seem to have found him back in the rooms he still occupied at his parents' home waiting for Sophia to agree to fix their wedding day, and I suppose set up housekeeping with him, though there is no trace that they ever pursued the details of the married life in which they were never to be joined. I see him with his recent purchase at the bookshop, turning the leaves with avidity, finding something here and there, and finally some verses that rivet his glance. I can even look over his shoulder, for I have a copy of the very pamphlet, I suppose we should call it, he was reading. There are twenty-nine neatly printed pages, with special

type for names of characters cited, and persons mentioned.
The old long S that looks like an f is used throughout. The
whole is entitled:

> 'Strictures in Verse
> on Performances at the Theatre-Royal
> towards the Close of the Season of 1799.'

There follows a small print quotation from Shakespeare:

'The best actors in the world; either for tragedy, comedy,
history, pastoral, pastoral-comical, historical-pastoral, scene
undivideable, or poem unlimited. Seneca cannot be too
heavy, nor Plautus too light. For the law of wit, and the
liberty, these are the only men.'

Then comes the notice:

'Printed and sold by Bacon, Norwich; J. Wright, Picca-
dilly, and Robert Baldwin, Paternoster Row, London—
Hudson, Cambridge; Rackham, Bury; Marshall, Lynn;
Downes and Boulter, Yarmouth; Jermy, Ipswich; and Key-
mer, Colchester.

Price Two shillings and sixpence.'

Quite apart from the connection with my great-uncle, I
find this a most interesting discovery. It shows that bro-
chures of this size and contents were saleable not only in
East Anglian towns, but at two bookshops in London. Two
and sixpence was a far larger sum in those days and for this
class of printed matter, argues an expectation of remunera-
tive sale. The following 'foreword' (though not so described)
fills the first page after the title page, and description:

'The following Sketch, the hasty production of a few hours snatched from more important avocations, is sent into the world in the hope to convert abuses that are now increased to a most enormous excess, and to arouse the torpid frequenters of the theatre to a due sense of their own dignity by a recital of the mortifying humiliations they have undergone during the last Season with a condescension, so gratifying to the Manager, and so honourable to their sensibility and Dramatic Task. Should the author have erred in his observation, from ignorance of the laws of the Green-Room to which he is almost a stranger, he requests that his mistakes may be attributed to their due cause. He is aware that such a work can never be pleasant to those who are satirised, they will not fail to condemn him as an envious or morose observer of the merits of others. But let it not escape their recollections, that the performers are the servants of the public, and as such, amenable to the judgment of every individual for their public conduct. In committing these sheets to the press, the Author has been actuated by no other motive than a hope to reform what he wishes he could commend; indeed all personal considerations are precluded by the impossibility of his being ever known. As his apology for the familiar style in which these strictures are written, he offers this opinion of Vossius' Dicto Satiræ laudatur nontam poetica, quam pedestris ac sermoni similis, peneque extemporalis.'

I can see my great-uncle translating the Latin quotation, with a slight smack of the lips, for a working knowledge of the dead language was, in his time, one of the distinctions between the educated classes and the vulgar. He passed on, as I do now, to find 'insulted Sense' be-rated for allowing 'Folly' to flout Wit and Virtue, which had taught mankind to venerate The Stage. The 'Critic Maid' was summoned to 'bear her Sceptre and the Torch of Truth' all in stately rhymed couplets. The illumination invoked was to 'dispel the mists that cloud a mortal's sight' 'pierce the gay robes the slaves of Folly wear, And show all objects as they really are.'

This formidable opening went on to find much fault with Brunton, the manager of the Norwich stock company, both his presentation and his choice of authors, and the members of his cast. Particularly 'Lord and Lady Capulet . . . Came they from Billingsgate or Southwark Fair?' The delivery of the lines is sharply criticised, even the costume and carriage are described 'In dirty dress, with melancholy mien'.

The actors are accused of ranting, and their Irish accent is ridiculed at length. Great-Uncle must have been relieved to find the actor Dwyer, who had so often joined Sophia in programmes, praised. But the husband of Mrs. Inchbald is ridiculed for 'waddling' in *Henry IV*. Bennett and Phillips come off better, and again, Great-Uncle must have been pleased to see Sophia's associates given a favourable notice. But Lindoe was accused of imitating Brunton, and Moreton was a 'senseless rogue'. Chestnut got a good word as the 'starved apothecary'. The supers who made up the stage crowd also were condemned 'in sad array, a grisly band of half a dozen scene-men crowded stand'.

I have no clear idea as to what my great-uncle made of all this. I have a feeling that so much of his knowledge of the theatre in London as well as Norwich had been conditioned by 'going behind' in the course of business, and being perhaps disillusioned by the invidious comparison between the lovely lines to which Dr. Enfield had drawn his attention, and the sordid conditions of stage life, from which he so longed to deliver Sophia.

But I have little doubt as to his feeling when he turned,

as I am now doing, and found three paragraphs which dealt with Sophia in the warmest, if sensibly qualified terms. She was put on an equality with the good-looking Mrs. Brunton, the manager's wife, and I have no doubt that he soon turned over the few remaining pages, but stayed to follow up the footnote on page 25, which says: 'Miss Goddard, though far from the summit of professional acquirements, has yet all the qualifications which lead to perfection. But if she inconsiderately engage to represent every part that may be offered her, through haste, she will inevitably contract habits, which can never after be relinquished—Already the precipice presents itself. Miss G. frequently forgets herself and her character, which could not happen had she time and perseverance enough to give the necessary previous attention. She is one of the few whose genius promises greatness, and whose talents ought not to be neglected.'

For very different reasons, my great-uncle would have been only too glad to hold Sophia back from so much too much she undertook. I don't suppose he more than glanced at the final pages with their quotation from Pope. These are the lines that made him determine to take the *Sketch* to her that very afternoon.

> Fain would I 'female failings' lightly pass
> And let Aglaia lead them to their glass
> But injured Justice with imperious voice
> Arraigns my candour and forbids my choice
> Asserts a Goddard's and a Brunton's cause
> And, frowning, dares me to withold applause
> The fairy forms enchanted I survey,
> Confess their magic, and the charm obey.
>
> And see, to bind the spell and fix her sway
> With smiles she hither bends her willing way

Her artless, unaffected grace we view
And own the Desdemona Shakespeare drew,
Or should the Wartergh's wretched countess take
We sympathise with guilt for Goddard's sake.
But having seen perfection, can I bear
So good an actress should be forc'd to appear
In every character which scarce her haste
Allow to read—because 'tis in her cast?
Impossible! Nor is the man her friend
Who errors, tho' so venial can commend
I set her virtues at the highest rate,
But can, as well, her faults appreciate.

I hardly needed to glance at the portrait to see, in my
mind's eye, my great-uncle, with his literary present neatly
wrapped under his arm, finding his way across, past the
Guildhall, by Upper Goat Lane to Mrs. Curtis's house. I
expect he was summary with the landlady's voluble warnings as she let him in, and I have little doubt that as soon
as he was admitted to her room, he gave Sophia the *Sketch*,
opened at the verses quoted above, and sat beside her to
see delight and becoming confusion inform her looks.

'Dear John,' one can almost hear her voice, tender with
emotion, rising with delighted wonder. I have no idea if
she or her lover had any clue as to the authorship of these,
for her, handsomely laudatory, and not unpolished verses.
As I read them, all these years later, and try to reconstruct
the scene at Sophia's bedside, and follow the interchange
of loving mutual response I feel myself that the disclaimers
as to ignorance of the 'laws of the Green-Room', the admission that the 'Strictures' cannot be pleasant to the persons they identify, the deliberate statement of 'the impossibility of his [the author's] ever being known' are a camou-

flage set up to preserve anonymity, and avoid the reply or indeed some act of resentment that the very nature of the *Sketch* naturally invites. The lofty ideals that are claimed as promoting the conception and exertion of the piece, the attempt at assuming unprejudiced the 'duty of criticism', placed on the shoulders of the public, make me wonder, can the actors, the establishment, the detail obviously known at first hand have been envied or wished ill by the writer? He must have been local. He is not wholly anti-Brunton, indeed respectful to Mrs. Brunton, and most adroit in making the fault-finding not a mere grievance against all the company, or all the pieces that were played. Sophia, so far as we know, had no relatives locally, nor anywhere else. So there is no question of an effort to attract esteem for her, at the expense of her fellows. Then the footnote sounds as though it were especially planned to give her sensible and affectionate good advice. The whole episode is a mystery. I delighted in joining, at this distance of time, in the pleasure it must have caused the two.

I can well imagine Sophia motioning to Mrs. Plumstead, to settle her higher against the pillows, so that she could read aloud particularly the second verse, in which she is singled out, after a passing mention of her senior, the manager's wife:

'Listen, John dear. He's noticed my Desdemona. I think I really did please Mr. Brunton when I played that, to his Othello. And listen . . .'

I have a shrewd idea that she probably overdid her declaiming, and set herself coughing, and had to wait to control it, and receive remonstrance from Mrs. Plumstead and her adoring but apprehensive fiancé.

'I did get the Wartergh part across. Listen! This writer names me!'

She may well have ceased to read aloud the third verse which considerately takes her to task for the number of parts she undertook. She may well have felt an adverse if admiring note. I expect my great-uncle held himself back from saying: 'There, what did I always tell you!' In fact, if it were not so impossibly out of character for him, one does ponder for a moment if he did in any way contrive the whole publication. But I have no evidence that he was subtle enough, or that he had any friend or acquaintance capable or willing to compose the piece for him, and put it on sale at two London bookshops and all the East Anglian ones. I am left with the picture of Mrs. Plumstead standing, pleased but anxious on one side, and the adoring John sitting or kneeling by the cherished invalid's bedside, stroking her hand.

I think I can take him up, at the moment Sophia turned the other leaves of the *Sketch*. I can feel with him, as partly from lassitude, from the natural reaction after so much pleasure and no little effort, she saw what those earlier pages contained. I call on him to say what he then endured:

'Nephew, you have not mistaken the relapse that followed. It was induced by her generous comradeship with all the members of the company with whom she had played and bore down on her small resistance from sheer physical exhaustion.

' "Oh, it's too bad . . . he's making fun of them all . . . and he ought to know, if he has any sense, that the poor old supers lead the life of dogs, only not so well cared for as many lucky ones . . .Oh, John," she cried. "Look. He's put in the most unkind description of the costumes and scenery. Well, whose fault was it? If the audience were more dependable, and the prices were higher, Mr. Brunton and

Mr. Hindes would be able to pay the supers more and give them better costumes."

'She tossed the pamphlet aside, and pressed my hand, as though she needed the support I was only too anxious to give her. I hastened to agree in order to forestall another surge of irritation and bodily racking that any strong feeling seemed increasingly to produce. I hoped to calm her thus:

' "My dear, I have no notion who wrote the lines. He seems to have known how to get them published. He may be some ill-conditioned furnisher of theatrical goods with whom Brunton has had a quarrel. But the part which speaks of you, is evidently written by someone of education and distinction. And of course he is right enough. The only way to get the state of the Theatre Royal improved is to point out in what it is lacking, don't you see?"

' "Ha!" She turned moodily away. "He likes to rate us as the servants of the public. That's true enough. The servants of private masters and mistresses are more considered and better cared for!"

'I picked up the *Sketch* as it slipped from the coverlet Mrs. Plumstead was adjusting, and she noticed that with the generosity that informed all her actions:

' "John, dear," she patted my hand, "I am an ungrateful wretch. It was sweet of you to find up this publication. I suppose it will be bought by someone at the Theatre, and handed round. They can't be pleased, those who are so unkindly criticised. I do hope no one wishes me ill for the all too pleasant praises I am given. I do hope Mr. Brunton sees that his wife is properly appreciated, and that no member of the company supposes I had any hand in originating or even desiring such a piece of literature should ever be contrived. As soon as I am allowed . . ." She gave one of her pretty looks of mock resentment towards Mrs. Plumstead

... "I will go and see them all at the Theatre, and apologise to those who have been slighted, and clear myself of any implication ..."

' "Don't you get moving about or thinking you're going to the Theatre until Dr. Lubbock says you may!" was her attendant's rejoinder.

' "Very well!" I found it rather ominous that she so readily acquiesced in the prudent counsels given.

' "My darling!" I hastened to interpose, "Mr. Brunton knows me by sight, and if it gives you the least reassurance, I will call and see him on the way home, and take any message you wish conveyed, or repeat to him what you have just said!"

' "You are so good and understanding, John. You might even invite Mrs. Chestnut ... perhaps Mrs. Brunton if she is not too deeply engaged ... to call here and see me. Explain to them that nothing less than Dr. Lubbock's orders, and the discipline to which I am subjected as if I were a naughty child ...", this was to Mrs. Plumstead with one of those arch and winning looks that cut me to the heart, as it reminded me of her use of just such demeanour in her stage parts ...

'Mrs. Plumstead, fortunately a woman of few words, only returned a comforting smile ... and Sophia smiled back gratefully and went on:

"prevents me from joining them and saying as much myself. You might be so good, John, as to say what I request ..."

' "My dearest, I will go, as soon as ever you feel you have had enough of my presence ..."

' "Who's asking for compliments now? You know quite well that I can never have too much of my chosen ... do I make you blush, John? It's very becoming", and she relapsed, I was delighted to see, and hear in a light laugh.

'Nephew, I could contain myself no longer. "I am blushing with impatient feelings, my dear. Don't you feel yourself that it is more than time that the message I will so willingly take to Mr. Brunton, should be that you will be playing no more parts until the summer, and that by then, you may have become my wife!"'

'I manfully withheld myself from anything further, and was troubled to see in her a new brightness in the eyes, a spot of colour in the cheeks, that showed a further excitement of which I much blamed myself for having been the unwitting cause.

' "John," she said, "do you know what I would like?"

' "I am only too willing to learn."

' "Isn't there an artist who does miniatures? Nice small, clearly defined heads, that are often so much more telling than larger portraits?"

' "There are certainly some members of the Norwich Society who do portraits as well as landscapes."

' "Then do you think you could induce such a one to come and make a portrait of me?"

' "Of course I could. I will set about making inquiries this very day . . ."

' "It will be an occupation while I have to lie here useless . . ."

' "Never useless, only resting from activity that has plainly been too much for you."

' "It would be something to remember me by."

'At those fatal words, Nephew, I had the hardest task in restraining my emotions. What I felt must have been visible in my expression for she took me up with that quickness that was so alluring:

' "Oh, it's not mere vanity . . . though the things you sometimes say would make a stronger woman that I shall ever be, vain to insufferability. I mean, of course, that, if you will try to procure an artist of sufficient talent, he should do one of you, at the same time. Then we would always have a presentation of what we were like, when we were ..." and she dropped her bewitching voice to give the word all the significance that no one could lend it better than she ... "lovers."

'Nephew, I am so plain a man, honest I hope as Dr. Enfield tried to make me, but no match ever for Sophia with the intimate subtlety of a beautiful woman.

' "Why, of course," I blurted out, overjoyed. "What a splendid idea. I will set about it at once."

'She gave me an even deeper look, at the moment I took it, in my simplicity, for mere gratitude. I should have known better.

'I set off, that grey and wintry morning. I made my way by Chapel Field and came to the Theatre by upper Newport. The stage door was opened for me by Fiddament, and I threaded the ill-kept passages, between the dressing-rooms and the back stage. I was astonished to find a good many strange faces. Glancing at the unkempt list, which showed the cast of the *Winter's Tale,* the most recent performance, which had never been torn down, while the company had been employed in putting on the spectacle called *The Naval Review*, there was hardly a familiar name. I asked for Mr. Brunton, or his wife, to deliver my message, but none of the comparative strangers whom I accosted seemed to know where they were to be found, or perhaps were too unaccustomed to being asked by strangers that I had some difficulty in making myself understood. At length I chanced upon Bennett, who did know me. But he was evasive. The most I could obtain was a vague:

' "There are great changes going forward. I do not know

if Mr. and Mrs. Brunton are in the Theatre. You might ask
Mr. Hindes."

'This did seem to me a change indeed, but even Hindes,
whom I knew to be charged with some detail of management, was not to be found.

'So I had to be content, and put off trying to see anyone
more authoritative than old Mrs. Rivett in the box office.
Here I did meet with some degree of acquaintance.

' "And how is that dear girl?" cried the warm-hearted
woman, and without waiting for an answer she launched
out into the most gratifying praises of Sophia, in a torrent
I was only too loth to check: "We do miss her. You see,
Mr. Yallop, it isn't only her style in playing her parts. She's
such a friend to us all, well, you know, she even joined in a
Benefit to me. That was an indulgence wasn't it! And it
isn't as if she always felt like it. I've noticed how tired she's
looked these several weeks, and that cough of hers. But
she's just been going on, until I said to Fiddament, she's
doing too much, I said, and she's using up her strength. But
we are all so fond of her, we are glad she's laid up for a few
weeks. I hope you find her improving, Mr. Yallop!"

'Of course I reassured Mrs. Rivett, for of all things, I
knew how Sophia would dislike the notion of being the subject of lugubrious gossip, and in theatrical circles. I had had
ample evidence that there is little time or opportunity for
sustained and serious conversation, even if there were a desire for it, which is not always the case. The disjointed
green-room talk, the hasty mutterings of those who wait
in the wings to "go on", are all of a nature in which a few
broken sentences, especially about personal looks and pros-
pects, lend every opportunity to what can only be called,
without unkindness, hasty gossip.

'I got away as soon as I could, and returned home, and

began questioning my parents, as to the chances of finding a sufficiently skilled miniature painter. I did not say, of course, what had prompted such an unusual inquiry, and hoped that they might think it had arisen from some demand of one of our customers. I doubt very much if they were deceived, but they were so fond of Sophia and ready to further any project I proposed that my father told me what he could:

' "There's Robert Ladbrooke in Scoles Green. He might do something for you, or at least tell you who could. He's a crusty customer, but I've never had a downright quarrel with him, and if you tell him who you are, and make it plain you intend to pay his price, I dare say he might be induced. Then there's Ninham and Sillett and perhaps Thirtle. That family are all in the painting line. I don't know that he himself wants to do such small matters as miniatures, but some of the pupils do flower pieces beautifully and I have no doubt would listen to a request. They are easier to get on with, they don't think so much of themselves as Ladbrooke does. Well, there you are. Let me know how you get on. If those names are no good, I might think of someone else!"

'So spoke my plain matter of fact old father, not without a knowing smile as if he thought he knew why I wanted so unusual a matter discussed.

'A day or two later, when I had been to see Sophia, and had been told that she was sleeping, and had better not be disturbed, I did as good Mrs. Curtis suggested, and instead of spending my time trying to cheer her sad invalid moments, and putting the best face I could on her condition which sometimes seemed to be alarming, I turned my steps to the northern ward of the City, where, beyond the river, many of the artists of the Norwich Society lived with their families, and their households, which often included several pupils. In an ample, flint-fronted house in Magdalen Street, not far from Gurney Court, whence Mr. Bartlett Gurney had lately removed his banking office to Redwell Plain, I knocked on the door which announced that Mr. Thirtle lived there, that he was an artist, and gave lessons in drawing and painting. I was admitted and shown into an upstairs back room looking out on to another of those city gardens that make with their trees, many of them of forest size, and the shrubs and greenery that accompany them, a prospect of Norwich, seen from a near-by eminence such as Mousehold Heath, have the appearance of a well-wooded park, into which streets of dwellings and the roofs of industrial buildings have been introduced. I have often wondered, since I have been hanging here, in effigy, how much of the various changes that have naturally enough overtaken a healthy and flourishing city, have changed the prospect with which I was once so familiar.'

Thus, at length, I felt my great-uncle was addressing me. Anyone may ask, how and why? The only answer I can give is the actual existence of the miniatures. One of Sophia in all her youthful splendour, which had so rapidly and endearingly charmed the stage; the other of my great-uncle, as he was perhaps in his thirties, far less mature and imposing than he grew to be in the life-size, half-length portrait, which I have called the Speaking Likeness, because it was that one, not the miniature, that led me to hold this long affectionate colloquy with him.

I tried to reach back, to share his poignant anxieties as the illness of his beloved showed no signs of mending. I feel quite sure, that she, if not he, was growing resigned to the precarious hold she had on life, and have little doubt that some such premonition caused her to make the request to which he had responded so enthusiastically. I felt, some-how, that I owed it to him, to give him an answer to the question which, though unspoken, I felt must have arisen in his mind, had he been the sentient being I had grown to feel he might be, from the vivid, almost articulate one his portrait displayed. And in my mind, if not in my voice, I tried to reply to him, so as to show my interest in the life he once lived, and to maintain the curious means of interplay that had become established between us.

My answer, to the reflection that he may well have made, as he was introduced into the upper back room that the ar-tist Thirtle used as his studio, had it ever been uttered, would have run like this: 'My dear uncle' (I thought), 'you are quite right of course. The modern industrial buildings, whose long and wide roofs, built to throw light on mechani-cal processes, and to shield operatives from glowing sun-shine, but make available top-lighting, have certainly changed the texture, as it were, of the City's appearance you see today from Mousehold Heath. But not so much as has been the case in many a newer and more rapidly grow-ing town of the half-century that succeeded your own time.

'For one thing, the outline of the Cathedral is still that of the biggest single building to be seen. Next in size and the height on which is stands, is the Castle. Both are of stone. Both are surrounded, by the tree-tops and leafy extent of the Close, on one hand, and the Castle Gardens on the other. Then, along the big southward sweep of the river, are the "Hospital Meadows", which preserve the playing fields of King Edward VI School, and give a green extent of many acres. On the horizon are the groves of Chapel Field and the incursion of the Town Close verdure that leads to the site of the old City Gates. There are also nearly thirty of the old parish churches, each with its grey tower, and the great

M

office blocks, which constitute the greatest alteration you would notice, are still within such compass, that they do not overshadow the buildings you knew, many of them centuries older. To sum up, you are quite right in your memory of Mr. Thirtle's studio, as being lighted from the north east, by a sufficient extent of open sky to give him the north aspect all artists demand. I and many another envy you having seen what the "workshop" of a minor but worthy member of the Norwich School must have been like. It must have seemed strange to you indeed!'

So I felt I should have spoken had our conversation been held. I like to think that anyone such as my great-uncle well enough known to have been citizen and shopkeeper, mayor and ward representative, finally politician on a scale that took him into the presence of royalty, and led to his knighthood as a supporter of Reform, would have listened to the account I was able to give with interest and sympathy. But the portrait maintained its reserved if benign demeanour, and I felt he might be saying in comment on what I told him:

'The Norwich Society, which I have learned from the conversations I have listened to in your room, Nephew, has come to be a matter of distinction in the world of Art, mainly local, of course, but ranking as a definite school, among the body of landscape painting of our nation, was, in those days, only in formation. I had first met Mr. Thirtle over some matter of framing some pictures for my parents. In fact, as I penetrated to his studio, I passed the shop on the ground floor front in which he carried on that trade, like any other busy shopkeeper. The studio was, you are quite right, Nephew, strange ground to me. I hesitated, hat in hand, among the half-dozen people whom the room contained, mostly younger than I, several of whom were engaged in working on canvas or panel, in oil or water-colours, while some were busy on the fitting and gilding of picture frames, a quantity of which, in various stages of completion, were leaning against the walls, or being propped upon easels or benches for convenience of handling. Some gave me a glance, some looked towards each other, as if to determine what I might be doing there, others too busy to take note of my presence.

'Presently, when he became aware that something out of the usual morning routine was afoot, there emerged from behind a large canvas which had to that moment completely hidden him, for he was naturally on the window side of it, at work, while I was confronted by its back, a little man of no great age, but as it seemed to me, bent and engrossed by a lifetime of leaning towards and peering at pictures in the course of completion. These had absorbed his artistic concentration to such an extent that, while, so far as I could tell, he was in possession of all his faculties, his sight was, as it were, distorted by seeing things not so much as they were, but as they made up a pattern or design, such as I learn the practitioners of the visible arts desire to lend to otherwise commonplace aspects of the outlines and hues among which we dwell. His hearing, again, though probably perfect, was attuned to discussions, lessons, arguments about perspective and chiaroscuro that made him listen for nuances that other more normal people would miss in conversation. His very gait was governed by that "painters' prowl" as I have heard it called, which overtakes an artist with perfectly good legs and balance, by the necessity he is under, of retreating a yard or so to judge of the effect of the last brush-load of paint he has bestowed on the work in hand, and then advancing, to correct or enlarge what has begun to be satisfactory, the same distance to bring him within reach of what he is creating. These elements in an artist's habit led him to accost me, in that curious half-waking fit in which all busy artists exist, and from which they emerge only with effort.

' "What is it? Who are you? What do you want?" he queried in the nervous jabbering manner of a preoccupied man, suddenly summoned from his immersion in the detail of a picture, to take cognisance of the living, non-artistic world in which he lives physically.

'Then as he succeeded in adjusting himself to the non-picture world outside, his normal faculties of a citizen, tradesman and native of the City asserted themselves. He took off his glasses, rubbed them, I thought probably quite unnecessarily and replaced them on his nose, and the contacts of every day imposed themselves:

' "Why, I believe I have the pleasure of speaking to young Mr. Yallop. How is your worthy father, young sir? And your partner, Mr. Dunham?"

' "Both well, I thank you, Mr. Thirtle."

' "I am glad to hear of it. Now, what can I do for you?"

'I explained my errand, and asked if he could undertake to make the two miniatures Sophia desired.

' "The young lady is indisposed at the moment, but is willing to see me! Yes, very well, I will call on her at Mrs. Curtis's, and see if we can arrange sittings for what you require. I hope she will soon be recovered. She has made a rare name for herself in a very short time. Not like us . . . do you think of us as limners, Mr. Yallop, making up a reputation of a sort, by showing people how things may appear, if they are seen with an eye to composition. A theatrical career is so brilliant, but no doubt subject to chance. I expect the young lady is the victim of overwork. They have to take parts when they can get them, I've heard. But Miss

Goddard is in great request, is she not?"

'I told him that she had been called upon to help her fellow members of the company, by playing for their benefits, and had severely overtaxed her strength and was directed by Dr. Lubbock to take a period of rest and relaxation!

' "Dear me, is that so!" I could almost see, Nephew, the mind of the artist already forsaking the world in which most of human nature lives out its daily life, and pursuing a new subject, for a work of Art. He went on:

' "Perhaps, Mr. Yallop, that is not altogether a disadvantage. I shall not need to fit my sittings in between the demands of rehearsals and performances. Miss Goddard will be able to receive me at her leisure. I have seen her play some of her celebrated parts with great entertainment and I shall like to make a portrait in miniature of so admirable an actress, and so charming a person, by all accounts."

'Nephew, as he looked at me while these words were said, I could see him calculating: "This will do me some good. I must ask for leave to exhibit my work at the next meeting of the Norwich Society!"

'But he did not admit what calculations were going on in his dedicated mind, in its narrow field of activity.

' "I hope I shall be able to provide what you want, Mr. Yallop. Then, if you are pleased, you and I can arrange to suit your convenience, and I will do the miniature of you, which you wish to have made as a companion to Miss Goddard's. I know of course that you are contemplating marriage. I should have congratulated you earlier on the fascinating choice you have made!"

'As I bowed my acknowledgements, once again, Nephew, I could see him shrewdly calculating: "This will be a very nice connection. These young people, if they are pleased, will put me in a good way of business, with the classes that keep and use the shops along the Gentleman's Walk."

'We stayed a moment to have a word about his usual charges, and I took my leave.

'I was so pleased at the apparent success in arranging to meet my dear girl's desire, that I took an early opportunity of calling at Mrs. Curtis's and asking if she was able to see me. I brushed aside Mrs. Curtis's downcast look and shaken head. When I was admitted to the bedroom and gave my news of Mr. Thirtle's proposals, I was glad I had been so brusque. Although Mrs. Plumstead kept a perturbed face and motioned me to be careful, when I said that the portraitist would be calling to arrange a series of sittings, the dear girl drew herself up and demanded her wraps, treating me with her most bewitching smile:

' "Oh, John dear, how good of you. How quick you have been. Is he really coming? I must look up some of my fallals and made a decent appearance. What do you think? A mauve ribbon, and that beautiful brooch you gave me? I've never had anything so becoming . . . and I suppose so valuable. You spoil this lazy lie-abed, John dear. Is Mr. Thirtle quick at his work?"

'For a moment the words struck me as ominous but I soon found I had mistaken her meaning.

' "Surely when the weather gets milder, Dr. Lubbock will let me get up, and go and persuade Mr. Brunton that I have not forgotten all the words and gestures I ever knew. So I hope Mr. Thirtle will be able to catch a tolerable likeness before I am allotted a part. You know, John, I believe I should get a fresh draft of health, if I went on tour with one of the companies that supply King's Lynn and Bury St. Edmunds, Yarmouth and Swaffham. What do you think?"

'I could not withhold myself, Nephew, from expressing my admiration of her at that moment. The very idea of the

miniature seemed to have rejuvenated her, if that is the
expression for one of her years. Her eyes regained the
sparkle I had so often admired, her lips curved in the
arresting "cupid's bow" that had captivated so many audiences. I believe that had it not been for the restraining influence of Mrs. Plumstead she would have dismissed me,
briefly, while she dressed herself in one or other of the
toilettes that so became her, and have behaved as though
she had never spent those miserable weeks in bed. But she
had too much sense of decorum and obligation to those who
had taken such care of her. She contented herself with many
delightful poses and proposals for profile or full-face, demanding my opinion, that the time Mrs. Plumstead felt to
be sufficient for her to complete our interview fled away,
and with many a longing look and backward glance and
wave of the hand, I was dismissed for that day.'

7

The Final Words

THE tardy East Anglian Spring was gradually establishing its milder airs and longer light while John Thirtle was making the miniature that my great-uncle had ordered. Trying to live again with him the last agonising weeks, I felt I understood, as I sat musing before his portrait, what it was that lent the air of reserve and resignation to it, which might otherwise seem unusual in the bearing of a man who was still to have many years of health and the prosperity which worldly success can give. Thirtle's work, on the other hand, presents the likeness of a very beautiful young woman. Taken in profile, it gives the outline and colour. It tells us nothing of the gradual weakening of which my great-uncle must have been the alarmed observer. I tried to convey to him the sympathy which, a century and a half too late, I felt for his manful attempts to keep up her spirits, when he had so mournful a task in reconciling his own to what he had to bear. He seemed to say:

'I tried to look in whenever a sitting had been arranged for the artist. My presence at least, I love to think, enabled her to overcome the growing malaise which I began to see, all too clearly, was overcoming her. She did not resent Thirtle's presence, her stage habit of making a fine and impressive figure before the footlights aided her. She is not shown actually smiling, but such scraps of news, anecdotes of the life that went on at the Theatre Royal, alas, deprived of her, seemed to amuse and fortify her, and this the miniature shows.

' "Who do you say these new singers are?" she would ask.

' "The Bruntons have gone to Lynn, have they?"

' "Give my love to old Mrs. Rivett."

'Then there were the humble gifts that an accepted lover such as I may be allowed to make. Snowdrops from the scrap of garden left behind the house and premises on the Gentleman's Walk, primroses that I could gather from the slopes of the Castle mound, the early violets that the stall-holders in the market put on sale, all delighted her.

' "John, dear, how sweet of you. They are lovely! Mrs. Plumstead, put them in water beside me."

'Something of this simple delight in the beauties of nature that had been so marked a feature of her drives in the countryside, a year earlier, when she was still capable of it, all helped to keep some degree of animation, a brave hope of getting better, and being able to return to a life of health and strength, all went to render Thirtle's presentation of her the charming record it is of her vanished beauty.'

He ceased, and I could almost hear the sigh with which he felt unable to continue. To help him to keep contact with me, I ventured to ask:

'I suppose even Dr. Lubbock did not know what name to give her disease?'

'I have heard much in this room, these many years, and gather that illness is now recognised by diagnosis, named and classified, and the remedies prescribed. In those days it was not only more usual, but it was kinder to a patient for whom apparently nothing brought any relief, to call an illness "a decline". That was what in fact it was. Dr. Lubbock employed all the skill and knowledge that was then available, but it had little effect. People lived by the life that was in them. When that declined, they "passed away" as was said, and while Sophia maintained so much poise and dignity propped up in bed or in a "chaise longue" beside it, her imagination took flight, sometimes when Thirtle was at work, sometimes when only I and perhaps Mrs. Plumstead were with her. She would take leave of me when I had to forsake her as if playing Juliet, as she longed to do:

' "Three words, dear Romeo, and good night indeed.
If that thy bent of love be honourable, thy purpose marriage,
Send me word tomorrow,
By one that I'll procure to come to thee . . ."

'and she would glance at Mrs. Plumstead . . .

' "And all my fortunes at thy foot I'll lay,
And follow thee, my lord, throughout the world."

'She would break off:
' "Oh what a shame, John, when you've been so patient with this patient . . ." and she would laugh and add:

' "A thousand times good night!"

'That would be, perhaps, when I was quitting her. But at other moments she would vary it:

' "O, for a falconer's voice,
To lure this tassel-gentle back again!
Bondage is hoarse, and may not speak aloud;
And make her airy tongue more hoarse than mine" . . .

'Thus reminded all too vividly of her actual state, she would interpose:

' "I'm not so very hoarse, this morning, am I, John? I believe I'm getting better . . ."

' "Now don't you try any tricks," would come the stern injunction of Mrs. Plumstead, and there would be mutual protestations, and fits of coughing, and when she had mastered them, she would take up again:

' "At what o'clock tomorrow shall I send to thee?"

'She would add ruefully, "I must be a sad impediment to your business, John, I don't actually send for you, there is no need. You are so good at coming to see me, poor thing that I am." Then Juliet again:

' "I shall forget, to have thee still stand there
Remembering how I love thy company" . . .

' "But you must go, now, John!

' ". . . I would have thee gone,
And yet no further than a wanton's bird,
Who lets it hop a little from her hand,
Like a poor prisoner in his twisted gyves, . . ."

' "I declare these bedclothes are as bad. I'm so tired of them . . .

' "And with a silk thread plucks it back again
So loving-jealous of his liberty!"

'And often she would bid me take my leave in the celebrated:

' "Good night, good night! parting is such sweet sorrow
That I shall say good night till it be morrow."

'And with that, she would wave me adieu as I reluctantly
sought the door.

'On other occasions she would choose to declaim:

' "Gallop apace, you fiery-footed steeds,
Towards Phoebus' lodgings; such a waggoner
As Phaethon would whip you to the west
And bring in cloudy night immediately . . ."

'Nephew, I dreaded her harping upon Romeo and Juliet,
for we all know what was the tragic outcome. And I hoped
against hope for something better in our case. But I dreaded
equally the grand declamatory passages, that I felt made
her over-exert herself.

' "O serpent heart, his with a flowering face!
Did ever dragon keep so fair a cave?
Beautiful tyrant! fiend angelical!
Dove-feather'd raven! wolvish-ravening lamb
Despised substance of divinest show . . . !"

'Nephew, I do not know if it was my fancy, but as the
condition of her lungs deteriorated, it seemed to me that
the lower notes of her voice became more sonorous:

' "It is. It is! Hie hence, be gone away!
It is the lark that sings so out of tune
Straining harsh discord and unpleasing sharps.
Some say the lark makes sweet division;
This doth not so, for she divideth us:

Some say the lark and loathed toad change eyes;
O now I would they had changed voices too!
Since arm from arm that voice doth us affray,
Hunting thee hence with hunt's-up to the day
O, now be gone; more light and light it grows."

'She would pause exhausted, while Mrs. Plumstead gave her water to drink. Then she would say:

' "He must have had some sad experience, our great bard. He knew so much. He might have seen us, John, during these delightful visits of yours!"

'Alas, Nephew, my visits became less delightful and more anxious. It was plain that she was not mending, in spite of the touching obedience she showed to the irksome régime to which she was confined.

'Yet both she and I kept up appearances. I never alluded to the Theatre and the parts she had played except with the tacit assumption that she would be resuming her life there. She, no less, always spoke of her fatal malady as an incident that would soon be past.

'At length, as we both knew in our secret hearts was inevitable, there came the fatal day, when Mrs. Curtis opened the door to me, with tears streaming down her face. I halted on the threshold a moment, but she motioned me to come in, and manfully controlled her voice.

' "Come and see her. I don't know that she'll be able to speak to you, but I wouldn't for the world be the one to spoil the last moment."

'Mopping her cheeks with her apron, she led me up to the bedroom door, opened it with precaution, and drew me within.

'My dearest was sitting up, supported by Mrs. Plumstead. Her eyes were open, but her gaze was already fixed on some view that is beyond the vision of living mortals. Her lips moved. I saw that her delicate hands extended on the white sheets, held her copy of the play that she had taken part in, I do not know how often. Her lips were moving, but her voice was too feeble for me to catch the words.

'Then her glance moved slightly and she seemed to perceive my presence. And one hand, relinquishing the volume, sought mine, she gave a little restless shake, as if summoning such strength as remained to her. Seeing this apparent recognition, Mrs. Plumstead rose, and drew back the curtain that was partly screening the dull uncertain day. And the words came, with a little fluttering effort:

' "Then window, let day in, and let life out."

'I do not know that she actually invited me, but I felt impelled to take the place Mrs. Plumstead had vacated, on the other side of the bed and to support the beautiful shoulders, and catch the audible words:

' "My Lord, my love, my friend
I must hear from thee every day in the hour;
For in a minute there are many days.
O, by this count I shall be much in years
Ere I again behold . . ."

'There her voice failed. She did not complete the phrase, nor add the word "Romeo" in the text. I like to think that she was still able to distinguish the playing of a part, from the reality of the life she was relinquishing. She knew I was not a player carrying out that famous farewell scene with her, but her real betrothed, whom she had loved in her wayward fashion and knew she had been loved by. Leaning

quite near I was able to catch the phrases she did not need
to search for in the copy she still held in her free hand:

' "O, think'st thou we shall ever meet again?"'

'I tried to mutter softly some reassurance, for if there
is one thing, Nephew, of which I am certain, it is that those
who love at first sight, as the saying is, and who make good
that inspired devotion of a moment, can never again be entirely separated by death, or any of the material conditions
that limit our human existence. This seemed to reach her,
and she gave me a little pitiful smile, and took up the concluding lines of that great scene:

' "O, fortune, fortune! all men call thee fickle
If thou art fickle, what doest thou with him
That is renowned for faith? Be fickle fortune;
For then I hope, thou wilt not keep him long.
But send him back."

'I believe, Nephew, that those were the last articulate
words she uttered. After them, there seemed to come a
slight rigidity of the face and limbs. I did not dare to move,
while I might be of the least support. But as I felt her hand
grow colder, and her breath no longer stirred the fichu
draped about her head, I gradually removed myself a little.
Mrs. Plumstead left the room on tiptoe, and returned with
Mrs. Curtis. We settled the reclining form against the pil-
low, the eyelids with their delicate fringes drooped and were
closed on those lovely eyes, and we all three remained
speechless in the presence of that final withdrawal.'

At this point, my great-uncle's presence in the portrait
seemed to grow not less dignified but dim, and remaining

as handsome and attractive as I had always known it, assumed a remote appearance, as if there were nothing more he wanted to communicate to me. This, of course, was natural enough. In face of the tragic end to his hopes of a lifetime of married companionship; however I tried to stimulate my imagination, I could not expect to derive from his image feelings which, at least for the time being, he had never been willing to divulge, and was all the less likely to be able to make me share, after the long lapse of time since that solemn moment.

Fortunately, Sophia's death was of sufficient note to call for a record, and I do not need to rely on my imaginary colloquy (if that is an adequate description of the interchange I had succeeded in building up with my great-uncle). The facts are set forth in the public prints of that date, and I can quote a description of rites that followed the last moments I had been able to reconstruct, through him, of the earthly converse of those 'star-crossed lovers':

'14th March,' runs the record: 'Died in St. Stephens Parish, Norwich, Miss Sophia Ann Goddard who came forward with so much success at Drury Lane Theatre a few years ago. The lady obtained a considerable reputation on the Norwich stage, and was so much improved in theatrical merit that her talents doubtless would have soon made their way to a secure establishment on the London Boards . . .'

The local Annals, compiled from contemporary Norwich prints, seem to me inevitably more intimate:

'The remains of Miss Sophia Goddard of the Theatre Royal, Norwich, were interred at St. Peter Mancroft. Mr. Hindes, the manager, and the principal actors attended on the melancholy occasion. The young lady had obtained considerable reputation on the Norwich Boards, and was making rapid advance to eminence when death prematurely deprived the theatrical world of an actress whose talents would have ensured her success on any stage. She supported with great fortitude and resignation a long and painful illness, brought on by exertions that her constitution was unequal to, and died on Sunday last, March 15th, in her 26th year, sincerely beloved and lamented by her family and friends.'

These plain but feeling words of a journalist doing his best do not need any assistance such as I felt I had received from my great-uncle, during the weeks in which I had been trying, and to my own satisfaction at least, succeeding, in reconstructing his love story and that of Sophia Goddard. I can see every detail. The chilly but dry and fine day of early spring with its promise, even in East Anglia's searching weather, of better to come. At the southern end of the wide provision market of Norwich, one of the largest in the kingdom, stands the massive outline of the principal church of the City's thirty remaining fifteenth-century or earlier parish churches. The building is so situated that the larger portion of the churchyard lies to the north, and does not seem to bear the unfavourable associations that the northern side of church graveyards often bear. That is where the fine 'altar' tomb which eventually covered Sophia's remains is to be found, some yards in front of the north porch of the nave.

It is not difficult to picture the officiating vicar, the Reverend Peele, pronouncing the last sad but dignified sentences of the burial service, and the slow, muted procession that must have emerged, on its short journey. There is no definite mention of my great-uncle, but I find it incredible that

N

he was absent, and I can see him walking with Mr. Hindes, the theatre manager, who seems, at any rate for the time being, to have been in charge at the Theatre Royal. The members of the company could not fail to be present, and I have little doubt that they showed that power of rising to an emergency that all the practitioners of the Art of the Theatre are so proficient in exploiting. They showed no doubt that nuance of manner of the profession, a little as though they had assumed the costume and learned the words, appropriate to the scene. The season was propitious, and there is every probability that fresh spring flowers, on sale only a few yards away on the stalls of the market people, were offered as a tribute to the lovely girl who would never play in their productions at the Theatre again. One can even trace the names of those present from the casts of recent productions, and supporting Mr. Hindes must have been Mrs. Brunton (if her husband was on tour), Mrs. Chestnut, Mrs. Rivett, Mr. Bennett, Mr. Lindoe, and all the others whose names I found in the *Sketch* that criticised them, mostly adversely, and especially in comparison with the so promising member of the troupe they had lost, in Sophia. The actor's life is inevitably precarious, its triumphs unpredictable, its practice arduous, its conditions trying. Many of that sorrowful little group must have wondered, in view of Sophia's youth and vitality, what the future held for them. What the notices of forthcoming performances show is, that as if her passing had dealt a blow to the successes to which her presence had added so much, most of the names of those with whom she had played, and who made up the mournful procession that attended her funeral, dropped out of the casting lists at the Theatre Royal. Some, no doubt found employment under Brunton, or the other managers of East Anglian playhouses, that seem to have had some years of modest prosperity, at Bury St. Edmunds, King's Lynn, Yarmouth, and as far afield as Colchester and Cambridge. Some sort of theatrical life was to be found even in the lesser market towns. It is not many years since one still came across buildings of fair size and no obvious commercial use, in Aylsham, and Dereham and Swaffham, or Thetford and Stowmarket, long since turned into warehouses or clubs for Boys' Brigades or Boy Scouts. Old inhabitants would sometimes account for them by remembering:

'Oh, that was the old theatre!' The tradition of *Maria Martin, or The Murder in the Red Barn* and other pieces of local association and sufficiently gruesome 'drama' for long were the only public attraction in pre-cinema days and before television.

It was perhaps fortunate that the group of dedicated 'troupers' who paid their last respects to Sophia, were not gifted with second sight, and little inclined by tradition and hard experience of the profession to look far beyond the next casting. If they thought about the future at all, it must have been with that touching faith without which perhaps the whole act of 'mumming' as they love to call it, would hardly persist. That somewhere, somehow, there must exist a manager genial to the point of generosity, on a basis, quite visionary, of solid permanent financial support, who will welcome them, admire their ability, give them parts in long continuous runs, and above all, pay them punctually, liberally and cheerfully.

Little could those who gathered on that March morning, and doubtless were prepared to put up a cheerful and eager face to their future, foresee that the Theatre Royal, in Norwich, depended on the then flourishing textile trade, on whose handloom weaving of crêpes and bombazines, of Norwich shawls, and camlet near-waterproof cloaks. The day was some thirty years distant, luckily for them, when the fatal weakness of East Anglian conditions, the hundred miles that intervened between it and the nearest coal-pit, would cause its staple trade to forsake it, and be trans- ferred to districts where swift-running water, and very soon after that, steam, would accomplish weaving and spinning at a pace and in quantity that not the most active of hand- loom weavers could hope to rival. Little could they imagine the Theatre Royal, turned to the lower prestige of a music hall, and finally to house the continuous spectacle, the as- sured weekly programme, the mechanical expedients and routine attractions of the cinema. They would have laughed to scorn the notion that the theatre could ever become the alternative to a new age, when entertainment would be brought to everybody's fireside, and be 'switched on' at the turning of a knob.

And, such are the far and faith-demanding rewards of those who feel that no mechanical device can always and entirely replace the living performer, and the human ele- ment, that a century and a half after they had dispersed to whatever fate held for them in the year 1801, when they so sorrowfully said farewell to Sophia Goddard, there came to be such a demand for 'flesh and blood' entertainment, that amateur, and even amateur repertory companies, asso- ciations and clubs, played in many cases, what they regarded as the classics of their stock.

In this there arose a curious parallel between the 'living' theatre, particularly in Norwich, where for decades, a semi- amateur tradition was to grow up at the Maddermarket of Nugent Monck, and the long continuous and constantly renewed prosperity of Norwich. For it is odd but verifiable that places so old and settled have a quality that outlasts newer and seemingly more vigorous accumulations of population. And the Norwich of my great-uncle survived the textile trades' decline. The old administrative centre, the cattle and corn market of a wide agricultural area, the handiness of a population whose very fingers were possessed of skills that came from generations of special use and cannot be learned in a single generation, and are capable of transfer to new uses, have continued to make the old regional capital more prosperous than it ever was, when the great wars came to an end and the long era of 'Peace and Prayers', as its members delightedly called it, was to dawn.

Little could Sophia's colleagues imagine what in a hundred and fifty years, Norwich was to become. Let us follow them as they disperse on that March morning. Even the date was contradicted by the printed notices of the occasion. Some gave the day as the Saturday, some as the Sunday. That we can forgive. The happier feature of the account is that, in an old established centre of theatrical representation such as Norwich, there is none of the facile jeering at a theatrical event that might have arisen in places where 'show people' were still regarded as 'vagabonds', legally outlaws, as Nugent Monck loved to announce that he himself was, in spite of his reputation, shown by the invitations he received to produce in places as far apart in distance and traditions, as New York and Vienna. The company playing at the Theatre Royal was still sure of its notices in the *Norwich Mercury* and was destined to go on, with many ups and downs, incursions of the music hall and the cinema, and in the nineteen-sixties to receive the recognition of an ambitious project, that a Civic Theatre should be built and used for productions that would have to be subsidised from official sources. So, one may say Sophia Goddard did not die in vain. Something of the lustre she shed not only on local playing, but on the stage generally, was to live and continue.

But there is something else which has made me want to tell this true story, with such filling-in of the gaps that local history does not scruple to leave in a local record. The story of John Harrison Yallop and his Sophia might well be dismissed as an ordinary, pretty tragedy making its limited appeal, too usual in its features to be noteworthy. But it is not like that at all, and Sophia's very pathetic demise happens to make all the difference.

What was it that took place, once the brief ceremony just outside the porch of the Church of St. Peter Mancroft was concluded? John Harrison Yallop turned away, sorrowful enough, heartbroken one may well believe, when one gazes at the miniature of a beautiful young woman, her appearance enhanced by the training in presentation she had received. Some friend, or member of the family that surrounded him, one hopes took his arm and led him home.

Now the obvious and ordinary sequel would surely be that a young middle-aged man, with a good business (look at the advertisement in the *Norwich Mercury*) on the proceeds of which he was anxiously expecting to form a comfortable home for his betrothed, would be reduced to despair, even to mental and physical deterioration by the shock of her untimely death. John Harrison Yallop was made of other stuff.

I have often longed to ask him.

'Did you feel that you owed it to her, not to have been cast down, as you had every reason to be, but that you should, as it were, offer to her memory the constant and increasing prosperity that would have been so thankfully lavished on her wants, had she survived?'

He does not seem to need to reply. The portrait looks as

if I ought to have taken that for granted. For he went on. He and his partner soon branched out from the limited scope of the trade of jeweller and dealers in precious metals and stones in which they had originally engaged. What astonishes me is the very general nature of the new lines of business that they were ready to follow. What led to their embarking on the sale of tea, coffee and cocoa? I did not even know that such a commodity as the last was 'fancied' in Norwich of the eighteen-hundreds. But Dunham and Yallop advertised it and the others. Was Dunham a 'taster'? A tea-and-coffee business certainly grew up behind the corner of the Gentleman's Walk where it turns to what is still 'Davey Place,' named after a famous Alderman of other years.

When I seek to interrogate the Portrait, I get no very final reply. Withdrawn, reserved, as if he needed all his strength to control his feelings after what had happened to him, I can only elicit a look which might mean:

'There had grown up a demand for these articles and we were able to supply it.'

So they did. Perhaps it was not so strange that they went on, once they had formed a connection with the public that purchased for the household, that they began to advertise comestibles. It was the Gentleman's Walk, where Gentlemen who passed up and down, avoiding the clamour and soiled pavements of the market stalls across the road, might be on their way to Rampant Horse Street, where the horse-copers, the job-masters, the dealers in equine choice were to be found. Did Dunham and Yallop seek to skim off the better class of the trade, what we call 'delicatessen'? Did they provide for the routs and ridottos, the balls, the civic occasions? True again, there did, in later years grow up in Davey Place, a very considerable business in catering, that provided wines and jellies for banquets and At Homes, and soirées.

I don't know, and my great-uncle does not seem to feel under any necessity to make me aware, as I felt he did while he was still doggedly, at times hopelessly, struggling to re-build Sophia's health and perhaps persuade her to relin-quish the life of the boards that he felt threatened her.

Was it her death that made him feel there was no longer any point to be gained by making me aware of how he spent his time?

I do not grudge him his reticence, for there are plenty of public means to enable me to find out. In his later middle life he became a conspicuous local figure. We may ap-prove today his long support of the project of parliamen-tary Reform, which was to earn him his knighthood from William IV. Meanwhile his fellow citizens thought well enough of him to call him to fill the office of Sheriff and twice that of Mayor. We may forgive him that the other public question about which he felt so strongly was his abhorrence of what the succeeding generations came to know as 'Income Tax'. In fact he was a Whig of his time and sort. His brother-in-law Bolingbroke shared his opi-nions. They were what the semi-illiterate voters of their day called 'Blue'. That is, they wore on all political occasions the Blue and White of the Walpoles. The dear, funny old things now so long relegated to the dusty oblivion where we keep the memory if we are loyal to affection, and duly aware of what was done for us, so long before we were born, come today!

But one thing is not funny. It is poignant and apt to this story. Year by year, from 1801 onward, there was growing up, with a very fair share of modest good looks, even health and temper (I have several of her letters breathing affection and concern for those dear to her) a little child who became a growing girl, 'teen-ager' as we now call it, who bore the name of Sophia.

I would like to know what John Harrison Yallop felt as he noticed, and I am certain approved the development of his sister and his brother-in-law's eleventh child, his fifth niece. Did he ever tell her, to whom she owed her christian name, and, he must have loved to think, her share of some looks that might be pleasant to him, but could never compare with those of the namesake he had lost! That little Sophia Bolingbroke, upon whom John Yallop must have doted, married James Nasmith Mottram, the confidential head clerk of the Gurneys at their bank, destined to become the present-day Barclay's. When Hudson Gurney built his ample new Hall at Keswick near Norwich, and moved out of the upper storeys of that fine old Georgian house, James and Sophia Mottram moved in. They were succeeded by their son.

Anyhow the two brothers-in-law, John Harrison Yallop and Nathaniel Bolingbroke, attended at the Court of St. James, and Yallop was accorded the accolade that made him a knight. How pleased Sophia would have been! He prospered as well as any man could wish. Appointed one of the agents for the Government Lottery of that day, he sold, amid all the diverse merchandise Dunham and Yallop dealt in, the books of tickets for Lottery Subscribers.

In later life he married the daughter of a tradesman who, so far as I can discover, had been one of those who prospered by supplying the armed forces of the Crown. Why, no one knows. He did not need any additional means for amplifying his already comfortable position, but they must have been on good terms, for it is said, that on making up his return of lottery tickets sold he found he had one left, and she (or so the story goes) encouraged him to purchase it. This proved a fortunate speculation. It turned out to bear the number of one of the major prizes, and he found himself furnished with a considerable capital. This he employed in purchasing the Eaton Grove Estate, just outside the City boundaries, on the wide Newmarket Road. Here he built the handsome William-the-Fourth-fronted mansion on so ample a scale, that today it houses (with recent additions) the Norwich High School for Girls of the Girls' Public Day School Trust. All these facts are known from various printed records in which his life and acts as a well known and liked public citizen are set out.

There arises then a curious duality which I have never been able to resolve. Perhaps I do not want to for the two John Harrison Yallops make an extraordinary diverse, even contradictory character.

There is the public well-documented citizen who rose by hard work to sufficient comfort, that was raised to handsome well-being, by an unlikely and (in his case) unique gamble. One might laugh at it and dismiss it, but that side of him always had the attraction of his progressive and benevolent spirit, that gained him his knighthood and such popularity as caused him to be chosen twice as Mayor, so that his official portrait by Clint hangs in St. Andrew's Hall, Norwich, with the Cathedral in the background, amid the Harveys and the Stewards, the Colman and the Bullard portraits of citizens whom their fellows loved to commemorate in such fashion. It is more showy than the private family portrait by Hilton from which I learned so much. And there is another, almost violently opposing character, whom I have felt I understood and was proud to be descended from.

For the curious contrast is, that the public Yallop, loaded with good fortune, seen as I saw him, I feel from within, had another side.

He cannot have lived much at his fine new house at Eaton Grange. More oddly still, his wife did not live there. He bought a neighbouring property, and installed her in it, either from some deep emptiness that she, good if ordinary woman as she must have been (or why did he marry her?) could never fill. She died while he was in his sixties, so that her separate establishment cannot have been a mere provision made for her widowhood. He himself migrated to Brighton where he died in June 1835 having seen Reform triumphant.

But his remains are in the vault he shares with the Bolingbrokes in St. Peter Mancroft. Either by some earlier arrangement, or by the high esteem that he and his Bolingbroke relatives enjoyed, he shares it with them, with older members of the family and with his sister Mary, and her husband, his brother-in-law Nathaniel. He himself is commemorated on the fine 'altar' tomb as:

'... a person of fair pretensions and many merits, in his nature and disposition unaffected and kind, as a magistrate upright and just.'

There are many less pleasant things said about the departed and all the evidences go to show that these sentiments were shared by his neighbours.

But move round and survey the west-facing panel of the stone table. What is inscribed here? His wife, Mary Ann, or any member of the family? No. The words are:

This stone
is dedicated to the
Talents and Virtues of

Sophia Ann Goddard
who died, March 15th, 1801 Aged 25
The former shone with superior
Lustre and Effect
In the great School of Morals
the theatre
while the latter
Informed the private circle of Life
with Sentiment, Taste and Manners
that will live in the memory
of Friendship and
Affection.

She had been dead thirty years before (as they would have loved to assert) he came to join her. And those were the thoughts that he wished to perpetuate. The words are cut in stone and bear witness to this true story.